MODERN COMBAT SHIPS 5

Type 21

MODERN COMBAT SHIPS 5

Type 21

Capt John Lippiett, RN, MBE

LONDON

IAN ALLAN LTD

Contents

Previous page:
Arrow *through a wide-angled lens. Note that whilst the class has two anchors it has only one cable and capstan. Either anchor can be connected up according to requirements.* *MoD*

First published 1990

ISBN 0 7110 1903 7

Published by Ian Allan Ltd, Shepperton, Surrey; and printed by Ian Allan Printing Ltd at their works at Coombelands in Runnymede, England

In glassy seas *Ardent* carries out a light jackstay transfer of personnel with the cruiser *Blake.* The distance between ships for such an evolution is normally 80ft. *MoD*

Acknowledgements

Perhaps the most encouraging thing I found when embarking on the project of writing about the Type 21 frigate was the enormous enthusiasm and support I received from many quarters. Countless numbers have been involved in the class over the last 20 years, designing, building, sailing, refitting and fighting the eight ships that were built. All those whom I have met and talked to have enthused about the ships, and have been anxious to see a book record their unique character.

I am indebted to a large number of people who have helped me in my work. When looking at the origins of the class I was grateful to Adm Sir Horace Law GCB, OBE, DSC, the then Controller of the Navy, and to Mr Peter Usher OBE and Mr Anthony Dorey OBE of Vosper Thornycroft. They had much to tell me of the radical steps that were taken in the development stage, and were kind enough to put the extensive photographic library of Vosper Thornycroft at my disposal. Cdr John Bingham RN, of Ferranti Ltd, was generous in allowing me to peruse his scrapbook of Amazon's first commission, under his command.

I have received much assistance from the ships' companies of the Squadron, both past and present. All the Commanding Officers of the ships at present in commission have gone out of their way to help me. Those commanding at the time of the Falklands conflict were good enough to study the draft of the relevant chapter and to offer their advice, providing additional photographs that revive potent memories. My own officers in Amazon suffered my additional probes and requests whilst I pieced the book together and checked some of the detail. I am grateful to them all.

The book would not have been possible without the co-operation and hard work of members of the Fleet Photographic Unit, who allowed me to search the archives for a wide cross-section of photographs. In addition, I must thank Mr Mike Critchley of Maritime Books for his assistance and advice when putting together this book into its present form.

My wife, Jenny, has put up with a lot. Well do I remember arriving home late one Friday evening and pressing on her my latest chapter. She fell asleep over the first paragraph! Notwithstanding this one lapse she has given unstinting support, and has been most constructive in pointing out what needs to be translated into layman's language. Since she is the only person capable of reading my writing, to her has also fallen the task of typing this book, for which she has my grateful thanks.

Amazon sails on. Will this silhouette be seen at sea in the 21st century? *MoD*

Glossary

AA	Anti Aircraft	NAAFI	Navy, Army and Air Force Institute
AAMR	After Auxiliary Machinery Room	NAVOCFORMED	Naval On Call Force Mediterranean
AER	After Engine Room	NGS	Naval Gunfire Support
AIO	Action Information Organisation		
AMP	Assisted Maintenance Period	OTHT	Over The Horizon Targeting
AOA	Amphibious Objective Area	PWO	Principal Warfare Officer
ASW	Anti Submarine Warfare		
		RFA	Royal Fleet Auxiliary
CAAIS	Computer Assisted Action Information System	RFL	Rocket Flare Launcher
CBG	Carrier Battle Group	SAR	Search and Rescue
CIWS	Close In Weapon System	SCC	Ship Control Centre
CODAG	Combined Diesel and Gas	SCOT	Satellite Communications Terminal
COGOG	Combined Gas or Gas		
CPO	Chief Petty Officer	SHP	Shaft Horse Power
CPP	Controllable Pitch Propeller	SMP	Self Maintenance Period
		SSM	Surface to Surface Missile
DC	Damage Control	STANAVFORLANT	Standing Naval Force Atlantic
DED	Docking and Essential Defects	STWS	Ship Torpedo Weapon System
ESM	Electronic Support Measures	TANS	Tactical Air Navigation System
FAMR	Forward Auxiliary Machinery Room	UHF	Ultra High Frequency
FER	Forward Engine Room	VHF	Very High Frequency
FLYEX	Flying Exercise	VT	Vosper Thornycroft
GRP	Glass Reinforced Plastic		
GWS	Guided Weapon System	WEM	Weapon Engineering Mechanic
HF	High Frequency	WEO	Weapon Engineering Officer
HOD	Head of Department		
IFF	Identification Friend or Foe	XO	Executive Officer
LMA	Leading Medical Assistant		
LPT	Leading Physical Trainer		
MAA	Master at Arms		
MEO	Marine Engineering Officer		
MoD	Ministry of Defence		
MEM	Marine Engineering Mechanic		

1 From a Different Stable

Postwar Frigate Development

Frigate development in the Royal Navy after World War 2 made steady and predictable progress over two decades. Destroyers that had seen war service were converted into Type 15 frigates, and the 'Loch' class frigate of the same generation continued as a Second Rate Anti-Submarine frigate. The 1950s saw the development of specialist frigates such as the 'Leopard' and 'Salisbury' Anti-Aircraft and Aircraft Direction diesel-powered frigates. Anti-submarine duties called for larger classes, and the Type 12 'Whitby' and 'Rothesay' steam-powered frigates, supplemented by the much smaller Type 14 'Blackwood' class, were built for this purpose. At the end of the decade General Purpose frigates became the vogue: the 'Leander' class developed directly from the Type 12, and seven 'Tribal' class frigates were built to a novel design. The latter utilised gas turbines to give sustained bursts of high speed.

It was the 'Leander' class that became the mainstay of the RN frigate navy over the 1960s and 1970s. A highly successful design, 26 of them were built for the Royal Navy, and a considerable number for other navies worldwide. The history of the class is traced in another book in this series, but it is against the backdrop of this class of frigate that the Type 21 frigate emerged.

Export Warship Sales

A considerable number of navies, both Commonwealth and others, were equipped with either British-built or British-designed warships after 1945. A glance through any copy of *Jane's Fighting Ships* of that time reveals many familiar silhouettes of earlier classes, but as fighting forces contracted money became scarcer, and as Britain lost both the remnants

Bottom:
The VT Mk 5 frigate shows the distinct lines from which the Type 21 developed. Four of these were built for the Iranian Navy. At 1,500 tonnes and 94m in length, they had an amazing 39kt.
Vosper Thornycroft

Above right:
The VT Mk 7 followed, being slightly larger. The increased length and tonnage gave improved sea-keeping ability and a greater range. Only one was built, for Libya in 1973. *Vosper Thornycroft*

Right:
Developed at around the same time as the Type 21s were the VT Mk 10 frigates, of which six were built for Brazil. Displacing over 3,600 tonnes, they were larger than their UK counterparts. The Anti-submarine version shown here had a Bofors twin 375mm A/S rocket launcher forward of the bridge, an Ikara anti-submarine long-range rocket system aft, and STWS torpedo tubes. She had both hull-mounted and variable-depth sonars, and carried a Lynx helicopter. *Vosper Thornycroft*

of the Empire and her maritime supremacy, so it became increasingly difficult to sustain an export market in warships.

Shipbuilding was in recession, and the warship building yards struggled for survival. Two firms that kept up the initiative with success were Yarrow & Co Ltd, Scotstoun, and Vosper Ltd at Portsmouth. The former yard had built more frigates for the RN and Commonwealth Navies since 1945 than any other UK company. It had also built a frigate for the Royal Malaysian Navy. Vosper's had opened the market in smaller patrol craft and MTBs,

together with corvettes, building more than 50 warships for 15 navies. With its eyes on larger craft, Vosper merged in 1956 with J. S. Thornycroft & Co Ltd (which had slipways of the required size), and progress was made with a design which became known as the Mk 5 frigate; this was developed as a joint venture with Vickers.

Vosper Thornycroft were rewarded with success. The placing of an order for four Mk 5 frigates by the Government of Iran marked the beginning of a privately designed series of frigates. Next followed the Mk 7 frigate for the

Royal Libyan Navy, and the Mk 10 frigate arrived some four years later, being the largest warship export order for the UK since 1945 designed and built by a private company.

It was from this stable that the Type 21 frigate emerged for the Royal Navy.

The Redesign of the Shape of the RN Surface Fleet

British defence policy was undergoing a considerable upheaval during the mid-1960s, involving a withdrawal from East of Suez and the cancellation of the new aircraft carrier programme. The Royal Navy's role was reassessed and redirected towards the NATO sea areas. The structure of the fleet was reconfigured away from the assumption that its air defence could be provided by carrier-borne aircraft and the future fleet was based on three classes of surface warship:

● An AAW destroyer fitted with Seadart. This became the 'Sheffield' class Type 42 destroyer.
● An ASW frigate to replace the 'Leander'. This became the Type 22 frigate.
● An ASW cruiser to provide command and control facilities to carry a force of ASW helicopters. This became the 'Invincible' class.

The Type 42 and ASW cruiser took priority within the MoD and with the Royal Corps of Naval Constructors. The Type 22 was a longer-term project, but by 1967 the 'Leander' design was 10 years old, and there were many developments to incorporate in a new class of frigate.

'The Controller's Frigate'

At the same time that the RN was reshaping its fleet, the Royal Australian Navy was looking for a new frigate, and had asked Y-ARD (Yarrow-Admiralty Research Department) for a preliminary design. The Controller of the Navy, Adm Sir Horace Law, was particularly keen to back any effort to keep the RAN with British-designed ships, for they had already switched to the USA for their guided missile destroyers in the early 1960s. Adm Law got the Admiralty Board's approval to be associated with the new frigate study, and it became an early collaborative venture. Vosper Thornycroft, who had for some time been pressing the MoD to take up Vosper's own design to help boost their chances in the export market, asked to be allowed to compete. The Controller suggested they form a joint design team with Yarrows, and this they did.

The Admiralty Board decided that they would progress the idea of a commercially designed Type 21 frigate as an interim measure until the Type 22 programme could be set in train. Not since the late 1930s, when HM ships *Brecon* and *Bressinden* were designed and built by Thornycroft had private enterprise been so fully involved with the production of a warship this size, for the Royal Corps of Naval Constructors (RCNC) had undertaken all such work.

The timescale for drawing up the requirements for a warship, designing and building it and then sending it to sea for trials normally takes up to 10 years. The speed at which the Type 21 went through this process is remarkable. In December 1967 the private builders were invited to design a patrol frigate. The payment for this was to be £100,000, repayable if the design was subsequently taken up. Vosper Thornycroft took the lead with Yar-

Above:
A model of the proposed Type 21 shows her clean lines. A Wasp helicopter is shown on deck, and it can be seen that the original design had a partially enclosed quarterdeck. The half deck forward of the bridge allowed four Exocet missiles to be mounted there later in the life of the Type 21.
Vosper Thornycroft

Right:
HMS *Amazon's* keel is laid at Woolston Yard, Southampton.
Vosper Thornycroft

row's, working from Portchester. A joint tender was accepted in February 1968, and the Staff Requirements were laid down in the first half of that year. They were for a vessel of about 2,500 tons which:

- was fully seaworthy and capable of worldwide deployment;
- could provide anti-submarine and limited surface protection for trade;
- possessed a self-defence capability against air and missile attack;
- was easy to maintain and economical to man;
- matched foreign contemporaries in performance and fighting qualities;
- had an attractive appearance.

The Controller wanted a frigate 'without frills'. Having laid down that it should have the new 4.5in gun, the Seawolf missile system, 184 sonar and the Lynx helicopter for its arma-ment, it was to have the identical propulsion system to the Type 42. Even in 1968 there was still controversy over whether computers should be analogue or digital. The latter won the day and the *Computer Assisted Action Information System* (CAAIS) was chosen as the computer system to be used, smaller and less sophisticated than the system being designed for the Type 42s.

A common feature in the birth of a warship is that all specialisations have an understandable desire to get their latest equipment onboard and, as dictated by the fast pace of technology, updated during the design and build phase. Inevitably this leads to an escalation of cost, increase in weight and delay in end-result. The Type 21 was not exempt from such pressures. By mid-1968 the Admiralty Board, under pressure from both the Controller and the companies, had approved the Staff Require-ments and the design was completed by September 1968. This amazing feat was

Above left:
The ship was built on an open slipway. This photograph gives a good idea of the midships section of the ship and the height of the decks. *Vosper Thornycroft*

Above:
Nearer completion, the ship is now fully recognisable. The bridge windows have yet to be cut. *Vosper Thornycroft*

achieved because of the commercial aspect of the project, and also the rigid timetable imposed by the Controller. Inevitably this fast pace cut short protracted discussion, and some arbitrary decisions had to be made. The commercial aspect dictated that proven and available hardware should be used wherever possible, but due consideration was given to the design being able to incorporate new equipment when it became available. Thus the Seacat missile system was fitted whilst Seawolf was being developed, and provisions were made for the fitting of torpedo tubes at a later date. Strangely, there was no mention made of the fitting of a surface-to-surface missile, though the Iranian Mk 5 frigate had a Contraves SSM. The RN had no such weapon in service, and although Hawker Siddeley had started on an anti-surface missile fired from either a submarine or a surface warship there was none available in the foreseeable future.

Adm Law recalls that many on the Naval Staff were not in favour of the Type 21. However, he fought through the concept and it found favour with the then Navy Minister who was keen on foreign sales and liked the price, which was put at £7 million. Within the Ministry of Defence the class was nicknamed 'the Controller's frigate'.

Design

The design of the Type 21 proved controversial in several areas. The RCNC was tasked to ensure the design was acceptable for service with the RN, and there was considerable debate over stability, the use of aluminium and the structural strength of the class.

To improve stability the design was lengthened by some 18ft, and broadened to incorporate newly-defined standards.

Aluminium was used extensively in the Type 21s construction. The use of this material was reasonably widespread after World War 2.

CA destroyers and the Type 15s both used it in their upperworks, as, to a lesser extent, did the 'County' class guided missile destroyers. In terms of weight saving, and therefore of stability and speed, it had considerable advantages, although it was more costly than steel plating. However, it had the disadvantage of having a lower melting point (650°C against 1,500°C for steel), and this meant that a serious fire onboard could melt the superstructure.

Type 21s have an aluminium superstructure above Number One deck, the first continuous deck. A 50% saving in weight over a steel structure was achieved. Despite the RN's previous use of aluminium, considerable objections were made to the Type 21 design, and sensible precautions were insisted upon by Director General Ships. These included the provision of steel ladders and important bulkheads, insulation of other bulkheads, and the fixed automatic spray system for fire fighting in all compartments above Number One deck.

It is said that 'a warship is engineering's greatest compromise', and the advantages of aluminium must be weighed against the disadvantages. Experience, 20 years on, has tipped the scales towards all-steel ships, and there is now a search for a light, fire-retardant material such as GRP for superstructures.

The structural strength of the design was subject to criticism, and *Amazon* received some further strengthening after her sea trials. Later in their lives all the ships had their steel hulls 'stiffened' by the bolting on of thicker plate.

Left:
Ready for launch. The large funnel is in place covering the gas turbine uptakes. The forward bridge screen on 01 deck has a door which led to a seamanship gear store. This was later removed.
Vosper Thornycroft

13

Above:
Going down the slipway.
Amazon **took nearly one minute before sliding into the water.** *MoD*

Right:
Afloat at last, the chocks float away and restraining wires hold her bow while a tug moves in towards her stern.
Vosper Thornycroft

On seakeeping the design was a departure from the much-acclaimed 'Leander's' hull shape, which was believed to be particularly good. The knuckle forward differed from the 'Leander's' break at the mid-point of the forecastle. It was laid down in the criteria that seakeeping qualities had to be comparable to those of the 'Leander', and predictions showed them to be so, if not very slightly better. Certainly the author has served in both classes of ship and has found this to be the case.

Appearance

The Naval Staff Requirement included that the class be good-looking, and few can deny that it is so — probably the best-looking warship in the Royal Navy since the war. VT's influence is noticeable: even the step between forecastle and bridge (once known as B Gundeck) was retained although no weapon system other than the 3in chaff launcher was sited there at the time. How far-sighted this was proved to be when Exocet arrived in the Fleet.

Complement and Accommodation

The complement of the Type 21 widened the range of controversy. The Australians, who had initiated the design, insisted on a ship's company of no more than 120, less than half that of a 'Leander'. The Second Sea Lord's department believed that the ship could not be run and fought by this number, and held out for 200 plus. A compromise was reached, and the complement was put at 170, with accommodation fixed at 193 bunks to allow for a training margin.

Accommodation was planned to follow RN standards, and provide the same area per man that the 'Leander' had. The day after the contract was placed, the Controller rang up VT to ask if they could use the same space but

Left:
Ambuscade was the first of the Yarrow-built Type 21s, seen here at her launch on the Clydeside. *MoD*

Below:
Amazon shows her paces during sea trials. Before she gained extra displacement from additional weapons, equipment and ballast, she could manage well over 30kt. The black smoke was a problem caused by the Olympus gas turbines before measures were taken to prevent it. *MoD*

Above:
Sea trials in *Amazon*'s first commission. The 182 torpedo decoy is being prepared for streaming and can be seen hoisted on the dedicated davit on the quarterdeck. *Vosper Thornycroft*

Bottom:
Early days of *Alacrity* on sea trials in Scottish waters. The handsome rake of the bow stands out well. *MoD*

provide new standards by approaching the design in some new manner. This initiated a study which resulted in the junior ratings' messdecks having a central recreational space around which four-berth sleeping cubicles were arranged. Thus were accommodation standards revolutionised: many would say they have yet to be surpassed.

Build and Sea Trials

Amazon was the lead ship in the class, built on an outside slipway at Woolston, near Southampton. VT had expected to take some three years in build, but this was extended to 5½ years largely because the propulsion system (also to be put in Type 42) was not ready.

The tonnage of *Amazon* had crept up during build, through additions put in by MoD and tight control on all the building specifications. She was now nearer 3,000 tons than the 2,500 tons of the design.

Her sea trials were lengthy but most successful, VT retaining a responsibility to the end of the trials. VT also had the enormous task of providing the support — documentation, spares and so on — for the class, and had to set up a large new department to this end.

Chronology

Pennant No	Name	Builder	Ordered	Laid down	Launched	Commissioned
F169	*Amazon*	Vosper Thornycroft	26/03/69	06/11/69	26/04/71	11/05/74
F170	*Antelope*	VT	11/05/70	23/03/71	16/03/72	16/07/75
F171	*Active*	VT	11/05/70	21/07/71	23/11/72	17/06/77
F172	*Ambuscade*	Yarrow	11/11/71	01/09/71	18/01/73	05/09/75
F173	*Arrow*	Yarrow	11/11/71	28/09/72	05/02/74	29/07/76
F174	*Alacrity*	Yarrow	11/11/71	05/03/73	18/09/74	02/07/77
F184	*Ardent*	Yarrow	11/11/71	26/02/74	09/05/75	14/10/77
F185	*Avenger*	Yarrow	11/11/71	30/10/74	20/11/75	15/04/78

Postscript: The RAN dropped out of the project for budgetary reasons after a defence review.

2 Weapons and Sensors

The concept of the Type 21 drawn up in 1968 called for a general purpose armament to enable the frigate to defend a convoy or other force against submarine or surface ship attack, and to be capable of self-defence against air attack, be it missile or aircraft.

The designed armament consisted at build of one Vickers 4.5in Mk 8 automatic gun, a quadruple launcher for the Short Seacat anti-aircraft missiles, a Westland WG-13 helicopter armed with air-to-surface guided missiles and anti-submarine torpedoes, two sets of shipborne triple torpedo tubes, and 2in *Rocket Flare Launchers* (RFL). At this stage in the life of the Type 21 it was envisaged that the Seacat system would be replaced by Seawolf, the next generation anti-air close-range missile. Most regrettably, this significant update never materialised, largely because of the expense that would have been involved: one could speculate that the loss of two Type 21s in San Carlos Water might have been avoided had they been armed as originally intended.

Below:
Pilot's view of *Antelope,* giving a clear idea of the deck layout. *MoD*

The balanced weapon outfit has been very largely left unchanged since build, but there have been a few enhancements over the years, the most significant of which was the addition of four Exocet surface-to-surface missiles. Before that, multiple 3in chaff rocket launchers had been added in place of the 2in RFLs, and after the Falklands War the number of 20mm Oerlikon mountings was doubled to four. Otherwise the class described in this chapter has remained remarkably stable in its fit of both weapons and sensors.

Computer Assisted Action Information System

Before going into greater detail of the individual elements of the weapon systems, it would be well to examine the heart of the fighting machine, the computer that brings together the *Action Information Organisation* (AIO) and the weapon control functions. But first a brief description of what is meant by the general term AIO. To fight a ship, the Commander requires a system of taking in all the information that is available to him, to form an understandable picture of what is going on in the area around him, be it on the surface, below the surface, or in the air. There are many

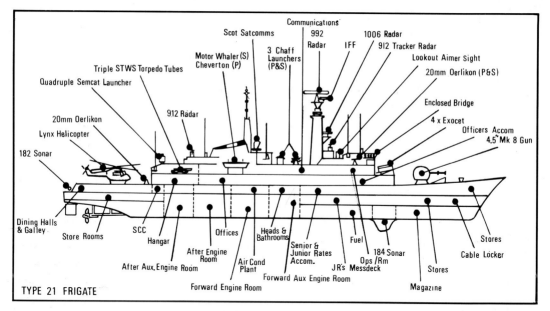

Communications

Scot Satcomms 992 Radar 1006 Radar

3 Chaff Launchers (P&S) IFF 912 Tracker Radar

Motor Whaler (S) Cheverton (P) Lookout Aimer Sight

Triple STWS Torpedo Tubes 20mm Oerlikon (P&S)

Quadruple Semcat Launcher Enclosed Bridge

912 Radar 4 x Exocet

20mm Oerlikon Officers Accom

Lynx Helicopter 4.5" Mk 8 Gun

182 Sonar

Dining Halls & Galley Stores

Store Rooms SCC Cable Locker

Hangar Offices Heads & Bathrooms Fuel Stores

After Engine Room Senior & Junior Rates Accom. 184 Sonar Ops /Rm

After Aux. Engine Room Air Cond Plant JR's Messdeck Stores

Forward Engine Room Forward Aux Engine Room Magazine

TYPE 21 FRIGATE

Above:
Type 21, Weapons, Sensors and Internal Layout.

Right:
A rare view of *Ardent* through a submariner's periscope. Her distinctive silhouette makes her instantly recognisable as a Type 21. This photograph was taken early in 1982 during a joint maritime exercise. *MoD*

inputs to build up such a picture: radar will give surface and air contacts, and sonar subsurface contacts. Secondary radar, otherwise known as *I*nterrogation *F*riend or *F*oe (IFF), can produce details of friendly forces through coded pulses. Visual information remains important, and intelligence and the reports of other units is increasingly vital. Data links provide the semi-automatic transmission of information from one unit to another. *E*lectronic *S*upport *M*easures (ESM) give bearings of enemy transmissions that are intercepted either onboard or by other units, which may be ships, helicopters, fixed-wing

aircraft or land-based installations. All this information has to be sorted, correlated, filtered and plotted in order to give the Command a clear, accurate tactical picture. Further, this picture has to be up to date, whatever the rate of information flow, in order to allow quick reaction time.

In pre-radar days the display of information was not too difficult, and simple hand plotting sufficed. Radar changed this, and a number of attempts were made using manual and semi-automatic plotting devices. These failed, however, when more than a few tracks had to be plotted, for the systems became overloaded. The digital computer arrived in time to assist, first going to sea in HMS *Eagle* in 1958 as a massive digital data system known as *Action Data Automation* (ADA), which developed further in the early 1960s on board the 'County' class destroyers. The weapon system was still controlled by analogue computers at this stage, but then the Ferranti 1600 computer arrived to combine AIO and weapon control into one comprehensive system. The result was the *Action Data Automation Weapon System* (ADAWS), intended mainly for destroyers and above. For the Type 21 a simpler system was chosen — the *Computer Assisted Action Information System* (CAAIS) — and this developed in tandem with ADAWS, going to sea first in HMS *Torquay* in 1972 for trials.

CAAIS is based upon the Ferranti FM 1600B micro-circuit computer. It uses Decca CA 1600 display units, which are each used by two operators. The picture is presented upon a 16in horizontal cathode-ray tube face, on which the operator can select to see a relative- or true-motion picture which can be made up from a variety of sources. 'Raw' radar, IFF and 'bright-up' auto-detection markers form the basic picture upon which can be added synthetic — or processed — information generated by the computer and selected by

manual keyboards. Such information would include track markers, labels, bearing lines, circles, ship's back tracks and velocity trailers and the like. Finally, two Tote displays show supplementary information on selected tracks, or answers to questions posed by the operators using the keyboard. The resultant picture can be very full and potentially bewildering, comprehensible only to the experienced operator!

Compared with the more fully automated system of ADAWS, CAAIS is smaller and simpler. It has limited automatic tracking ability and does not evaluate threats or assign weapons. As its name implies, it is an AIO system which is *assisted* by a computer. The degree of assistance is proportional to the amount of raw data fed in and the instructions it is given with which to work. It does, however, present the Command with a selected tactical picture and it enables the ship to be fought efficiently. Over the years the software package has been updated with new additions to enhance further its effectiveness.

Sensors

Radars

The main surveillance radar of the Type 21 is the 992, an Echo/Foxtrot band radar used for surface and air warning as well as target indication. The 21ft cylindrical radome is at the

Below:
Operations Room Layout.

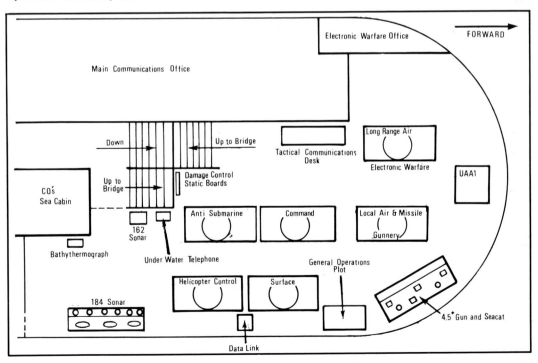

Left:
The foremast in its original state. The 992 surveillance radar is the largest aerial at the very top. On the same platform, and very much smaller, are the IFF aerials. VHF and UHF communications aerials are mounted on the yards below, and the navigational radar 978 is mounted on a platform set to port. This radar is used for helicopter control, and is offset in order to 'see' the helicopter as it approaches the ship from astern. Mounted on the pedestal in the foreground is the 912 tracker aerial for weapon control. The spike aerials either side of the mast look impressive but house only TV aerials.
Vosper Thornycroft

Right:
This view of *Active* shows the modified foremast with ESM aerials mounted directly below the 992 platform. The 1006 radar has replaced the 978 on the lower platform.
MoD

highest point of the ship, situated on the foremast. This radar can pick up air contacts out to some 70 miles from the ship, but surface contacts will only be obtained out to horizon range, which is in the order of 20 miles. Close to the 992, on the same platform but slightly lower and much smaller, is the 1010 secondary radar, the Identification Friend or Foe, which is linked in to the primary radar. This is the interrogator part of the system, which sends out the pulse from the ship. This pulse can automatically trigger a transponder in another unit, which then itself sends out a pulse in any one of 4,096 codes. The reply pulse is read onboard to give the identity of the contact. The entire process is controlled and interpreted by the CAAIS computer when directed by the operator.

For navigation and helicopter control there is another radar, the Kelvin Hughes 1006, and this is situated halfway up the foremast. It is offset to port in order to give radar coverage to the helicopter approach path from the port quarter: the mast creates a blind arc of some 30°. 1006 is in India band and has an excellent range and bearing accuracy; its range is to the horizon only. Originally the Type 21 was fitted with the earlier navigation radar Type 978.

Either 992 or 1006 radar can be selected on the displays in the Operations Room. The Officer of the Watch on the bridge, however, has a much smaller and more compact display called a JUD. This is placed alongside the chart for ease of navigation. He will refer to it frequently, and use it also for collision avoidance. Should the ship have to navigate in coastal waters in bad visibility the Navigating Officer will conduct his blind pilotage from the JUD. Further navigational aids include the Decca and Omega receivers and a satellite navigation system. The ship's log, an electro-magnetic log situated some 120ft from the bow and protruding 2ft from the ship's bottom, provides speed information to the FM1600B computers and the Satnav, as well as giving a visual readout on the bridge, in the Operations

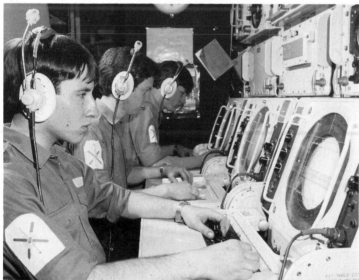

Room and in the Ship Control Centre. Two Sperry Mk 19 compasses provide ship's head.

Electronic Warfare

Electronic warfare forms a vital element in the make-up of a modern warship. Any electronic emission, across a wide spectrum including radar and communications, can be detected by a specially designed receiver. Naturally this is dependent on range, emitter power and aerial capabilities. Type 21s are fitted with *E*lectronic *S*upport *M*easures (ESM) equipment that is common to most modern RN warships. UAA-1, once codenamed Abbey Hill, performs the task of intercepting and analysing transmissions across the electronic spectrum, which includes most bands used for radar. It thus can be expected to detect not only the radars of other

ships and aircraft, but also of incoming missile heads. The successful interceptions of Exocet attacks on the Task Group off the Falkland Islands in 1982 were notably performed by Type 21s using this equipment.

The system is operated by one junior rating, and has a fair degree of automation. It breaks down the intercepted radar pulse to give its frequency, characteristics such as pulse width and pulse repetition frequency, and bearing. Individual radars can be fingerprinted, and UAA-1 has a library of standard radars against which to compare its intercept, and hence identify the actual radar and platform. Automatic alarms can be set for threat radars, and UAA-1 can feed its bearing information into CAAIS for display on all the tables.

Ships recently refitted have been equipped

with Type 670 electronic warfare jammers, which can be used in self-defence against enemy missiles.

Sonars

The Type 21 frigate is fitted with the Type 184 sonar for hunting submarines. Developed in the 1960s as a successor to the Type 177, this is a medium-range, 6-9kHz frequency sonar with a 360° search. An advance on previous transducers, which had to rotate to sweep all round a ship, the 184 has a fixed transducer with 32 staves which can transmit their pulses either together or in rotation. Such methods produce an 'omni' or 'ripple' transmission which is used in different tactical situations. The Type 184 actually consists of three independent sonars. Firstly, a PPI display which is similar in appearance to a radar set with contacts showing as a bright blip. Unlike radar, though, there is additional information to be had by the operator from the second, audio, facility. A doppler display searches sectors and can detect submarines from their doppler — the shift in frequency of the returning echo — and this doppler shift, together with ship's course and speed and bearing movement, gives a good indication of submarine course and speed. Finally, there is an HE display — Hydrophone Effect — which is simply a passive listening set. This listens for and then displays in bearing any noise made by a submarine or torpedo. This sonar will only

detect contacts at close range, and should not be muddled with the far more sophisticated passive towed-away sonars that can make detection at a range of miles rather than hundreds of yards.

Additional sonars include the Type 162 bottom-search sonar, used for overrunning a stationary contact to classify it, the underwater telephone, and a disposable bathythermograph which records the temperature gradient of the water — vital for prediction of the sonars' ray paths and their ranges. A Type 1077 sonar is an onboard simulator trainer which feeds in synthetic targets to the operators' displays. Finally, there is a Type 182 torpedo decoy that is mounted on the quarterdeck and can be streamed astern. This body radiates a noise into the water to seduce submarine-launched torpedoes that may be homing on to the ship.

Weapons

We have reviewed the sensors which detect the potentially hostile contacts, and the action information system which draws together all the information to display it to the Command. Naturally, the essence of a warship is in its potential to attack and defend — in other words, in its weapons. A general purpose frigate such as the Type 21 has a variety to give it a wide capability.

STWS

Anti-submarine warfare is probably the most important role. Having detected a submarine contact, the frigate can attack it either itself with torpedoes, or bring in another unit such as a helicopter or maritime patrol aircraft to carry out the attack whilst it maintains contact from a respectable range. Shipborne torpedoes are mounted in triple tubes on 01 deck abreast the hangar. These are quick-reaction torpedoes that are ready to be fired in an instant from the Operations Room.

This system, known as *Ship Torpedo Weapon System* (STWS), was not ready when the ships were first constructed, but was retrofitted to all but *Amazon*. Strangely it was never added to her, for purely financial reasons, and this anachronism is sadly felt in her reduced ASW capability. STWS 1 is the system fitted, but it has been updated to STWS 2 in other classes of ship. STWS 2 was fitted into *Alacrity* and *Active* during refits, but policy has now changed under financial pressure, and STWS 1 is starting to be removed without replacement. *Avenger* was the first to lose her torpedo tubes.

STWS 1 carries the Mk 44 or Mk 46 torpedoes, both US designed homing torpedoes that have been in service for some time. These torpedoes are also loaded on the Type 21's Lynx helicopter, which can be vectored over the frigate's contact by the onboard helicopter controller. In addition, the Lynx will in future carry the RN Stingray, a UK-designed and built weapon that is in the forefront of anti-submarine technology. The offensive power of the Type 21 will be considerably enhanced by the introduction of this weapon.

Exocet

Surface-vessel attack forms the next role for the Type 21, and for this the four Exocet missiles mounted forward of the bridge are the main armament. The initial design of this class did not include Exocet, which was still under development in France. Trials were completed by the manufacturers, Aérospatiale, in 1972, and the missiles were fitted over the next decade.

The system GWS 50 (Guided Weapon System) is a packaged system that has a high reliability and requires minimum maintenance. The Exocet missiles are ready to be fired at very short notice. All that is required is that the ship should point in the rough direction of the target, the approximate range and bearing of which is fed into the setting panel, together with the distance from the target that the

Left:
***Active*'s Lynx on deck. The torpedo tubes are trained outboard in their normal seagoing position, and the after starboard 20mm gun is manned.** *MoD*

F171

missile is to switch on its own radar. Thereafter the missile can be launched at the turn of a key. It then guides itself, switches on its radar to lock on to the target, and then steers an intercept course. A radio altimeter controls altitude, which can be preset to give a sea-skimming height.

The missile comes fitted in its own large container, which acts as a secure stowage as well as launcher. Its significant disadvantage is that it is not reloadable and cannot be replaced at sea. Four shots are all that are to be had, so one must be certain to have the correct targets. The missile has two solid fuel motors that take it to Mach 0.9 and give it a horizon range. The

43kg HE warhead may be modest, but the mass of missile following will add significantly to damage.

Further anti-ship armament is provided by the helicopter-launched Sea Skua missiles, covered in the chapter about the Lynx. A fall-back weapon system would be the 4.5in Mk 8 gun, which also has an important role in shore bombardment and a secondary capability against aircraft.

4.5in Gun

The Vickers 4.5in (114mm) Mk 8 gun first went to sea in HMS *Bristol* a year or so before *Amazon*. It is a development of the Army's

Top:
Amazon launches an Exocet missile. Four are carried, but they cannot be reloaded onboard. The missile is highly effective against other surface contacts. The next generation of warships is being armed with Harpoon in place of Exocet because of its greatly increased range. *MoD*

Right:
The Bay of Biscay lives up to its reputation. A spectacular shot of Amazon, taken from her Lynx, with the Exocet missile containers well visible in front of the bridge screen. *MoD*

Abbot gun, and was designed by Vickers in conjunction with the Royal Armament Research and Development Establishment. A breakthrough from previous mountings in the RN, it was considerably lighter (25 tons against 44 tons of the dual-gun Mk 6), being constructed from a glass-reinforced plastic/balsa wood sandwich of considerable strength. It used fixed ammunition: that is, the shell and cartridge were combined as one unit. Previously, 4.5in guns in the Royal Navy had separate shell and cartridge. The mounting design incorporates a simple ammunition feed system, having the minimum number of transfer points. Ammunition is transferred from the deep magazine to the gunbay, which also serves as a ready-use magazine, via a hydraulic hoist. Within the gunbay the autoloader then transfers the ammunition on to the

Above:
This view shows both the 4.5in gun and the 3in rocket launchers with their ready-use lockers in between. These launchers were later resited to allow the Exocet missiles to be mounted on this deck. *Vosper Thornycroft*

feed ring, upon which 14 rounds are stowed vertically. This feed ring then transfers the ammunition around to the bottom of the hoist, which is at the centre of the rotation of the turret, and it then is sent up into the turret. Here it is picked up by the loading arm, fused, and then rammed into the breach. The process, hydraulically operated at a pressure of 3,200psi, takes some two seconds.

The gun is designed to be operated from the Operations Room without the gun crew closing up. The rounds loaded on the feed ring are

Left:
Seen from inside the bridge window at the moment of firing. The 4.5in gun, firing at 25 rounds per min, can lay down extremely accurate fire in support of friendly troops ashore. *MoD*

Above:
Ambuscade, in pre-Exocet days, escorts a 'Rover' class Royal Fleet Auxiliary. The 3in rocket launchers are turned inboard, presumably for reloading. *MoD*

available at virtually instant notice, but, once expended, have to be reloaded by the crew. There are different types of ammunition, such as high explosive, chaff (which produces radar decoys), and Starshell. The latter provides illumination at over ½ million candles as it floats down on a parachute, burning for 40sec. Other practice ammunition is available for peacetime purposes. Careful planning is required to ensure that the right ammunition, or mixture of it, is available on the feed ring. If it is not, a delay will ensue whilst the ammunition is changed over.

The gun fires at a rate of 25 rounds per minute, and has a maximum range of 24,000yd with a muzzle velocity of 2,850ft/sec. Its range, accuracy, speed of reaction, rate of fire and weight of ammunition are all a considerable improvement on the previous Mk 6 gun.

Seacat

The Staff Requirement for the Type 21 laid down that the Seawolf surface-to-air missile system should be fitted. Seawolf was still under development, so the in-service close-range SAM — Seacat — was chosen, and this remains fitted to this day.

Short's Seacat had been in service with the RN since 1962, but the Guided Weapon System GWS 24 was developed for the Type 21 to give maximum flexibility of operation — a great deal better than the previous GWS 22 system.

The missile is designed as a close-range weapon, and uses radio command guidance to steer it on to the target. There is a variety of modes of fire which can be selected in GWS 24 according to the operational circumstances. To understand these it is first necessary to describe the system.

The missile is small (63kg), powered by solid-fuel propellent, and carries a relatively large warhead, which is triggered by either an impact or proximity fuse. The launcher is a single mounting, carrying four missiles which are manually loaded.

The associated radar is the Type 912, which can acquire and track an air target. An optical sight is slaved to this director and can track the target automatically. The rating controlling the Seacat sits in the Operations Room and fires the missile from there, deciding which mode is the best. The optical sight, a closed-circuit TV system called TVA2, can guide the missile all the way to the target or can be selected just to 'gather' the missile after launch, before the aimer takes control of it using a tiny joystick. Alternatively, he can use the joystick in the Operations Room for the whole process, or give control of the operation to the missile rating who mans the Pedestal Sight at the forward end of the Seacat deck. This is a small lightweight sight, not dissimilar to motor bicycle handlebars mounted on a pedestal, but with a joystick on one of the handles. This is an emergency mode of fire, but it can prove particularly useful when 'bounced' unexpectedly by aircraft.

Left:
The Seacat missile at launch. It has been fired through the skin that has protected it whilst on the launcher, and fragments of this can be seen around the launcher. The missile is controlled either manually or automatically, and is for close-range actions only. Although very dated now, it had a good record of service in 1982. *MoD*

Left:
Inside the Operations Room the Seacat and gun are controlled from the console shown in this photograph. Radar screens and computers give all the information needed for the Controllers to sight their weapons, and this they do by the use of the light pen. The gun is fired from the foot push seen on the deck, and the Seacat aimer's pistol grip and thumb joystick can just be made out at the far end of the console.
Vosper Thornycroft

Whilst the missile system is now aged and slow in comparison with its modern counterparts, it proved useful in the Falklands conflict, and is undoubtedly better than nothing.

Fire Control Tracker Radar

The fire-control radar for the gun and Seacat is the Type 912 Selina Orion RTN 10X. A commercial lightweight radar, this broke new ground for the RN, and has proved very successful throughout its life. There are two 912s fitted on the Type 21, one above the Gun Direction Platform forward, and one abaft the funnel. A Marconi CCTV camera is mounted on each tracker.

The tracker has the ability to operate in a hostile electronic environment, and can acquire and track targets automatically when 'indicated' from the CAAIS system. Control of each tracker is by one man in the Operations Room.

Small Calibre Weapons

In addition to the main armament, single 20mm Oerlikon guns were placed on either bridge wing, to give additional close-range

Above:
The two-man crew of the Oerlikon, this one being the port forward mounting on the bridge wing. Aimed by eye, it can produce a rate of fire with tracer bullets that may put off an attacking aircraft. It also has uses against small surface craft that it is not economical to threaten with larger weapons. *MoD*

protection against aircraft attack and to provide a deterrent to small vessels that did not warrant threat from the 4.5in gun or Seacat systems.

It was found in the South Atlantic that fire from the 20mm, readily seen by the attacking pilots because of the tracer ammunition used, proved to be a valuable deterrent against accurate attacks. This lightweight and cheap system was then rapidly enhanced by the provision of two further mountings, either at the forward end of the flight deck, or, in *Amazon's* case, on 01 deck, where STWS tubes would normally be fitted. Certainly the 20mm from a Type 21 in the Falklands shot down one attacking aircraft.

General purpose machine guns can be mounted at various points around the upper deck to add further close-range firepower against aircraft attack.

Communications

A vital element of modern warfare is communications, an all-embracing term which covers a multitude of functions. A warship must be able to communicate both with its shore bases and with other ships at sea. This calls for worldwide communications using *High Frequency* (HF) transmitters and receivers, or alternatively a satellite network using the Skynet satellite. The *Satellite Communications Terminal* (SCOT) can be fitted to the Type 21 when required by its operations. Two identical aerials are mounted in domes either side of the funnel, with an engineering cabin bolted on to the deck between them. A control console is then installed in the Main Communications Office for the operators' use. Communications by satellite is more secure in that the transmissions are more difficult to intercept. HF transmissions can be detected and a transmitting ship can be reasonably accurately located by cross-bearing from two receivers.

For horizon-range communications *Ultra High Frequency* (UHF) equipment is used. Voice or teleprinter messages can be passed either coded or 'in the clear'. Each ship is fitted with a 1202 *Very High Frequency* (VHF) set, situated on the bridge, to enable the ship to communicate with merchant ships in its area on designated international maritime frequencies.

Data Links

The speed of modern warfare is such that it is important to be able to transfer a mass of action information from one warship's Operations Room to another in very short time. Data links are designed to do just this, and there are several types in existence in NATO navies. The Type 21 is equipped with Link 10, an inter-RN link with a moderate capability.

The data link, tied into the CAAIS computer, is a serial transmission, medium-speed (1200 baud) link that uses either HF or UHF radio channels. Data link messages, using the slot method for reporting, are sent from one ship to all others as directed by an operator in the Ops Room. The other ships automatically receive, decode and convert to own ship co-ordinates, the information. This is then stored, and can be selected for display at any of the positions in the Ops Room, the track being specially marked to indicate that it has not been generated by the ship's own sensors. In this way a warship can build up an accurate and up-to-date picture of what is happening well outside the coverage provided by its own sensors. One ship can give radar coverage to an entire force while the remainder remain silent, and therefore undetected, on their own radars.

A further data link fitted in Type 21s is Link 14. This receives only, and displays on a computer terminal in the Operations Room a diagrammatic picture of friendly and hostile forces. The scale of this picture can be altered to give particularly wide coverage, thus allowing the Command an overall understanding of the operational picture. The Link 14 picture is normally compiled by the Tactical Commander afloat, or the shore headquarters.

Left:
Inside the Main Communications Office. On the left are the teleprinter bays which facilitate the reception and transmission of RATT messages both tactically and strategically. Equipment out of sight in this photograph includes a full width of frequency bands from LF to UHF. In the central-right part of this photograph is the unit which houses the Satellite Communications equipment (fitted for, but not with, in this picture). Satcomms provide a highly reliable long-range communications link.
Vosper Thornycroft

3 Machinery and Propulsion Systems

The Type 21 was designated from the outset an 'all-gas' frigate, the first to be designed and built as such for the Royal Navy. Previously HMS *Exmouth*, a Type 14 ASW frigate, had been converted to a trials ship for gas turbines. She carried out trials in the late 1960s fitted with the Rolls-Royce Marine Olympus TMIA, a development of the aircraft engine which powered the 'V' bombers and TSR2.

The machinery package was designed to be the same as that of the Type 42 destroyer, which was undergoing design and construction at much the same time. Being a smaller ship some changes were necessary, but Vosper's previous experience in fitting gas turbines into the Mk 5 Iranian frigate helped solve the problems encountered. The all-gas concept produced considerable power from relatively light engines, and the commonality with the Type 42 ensured a reduction in the training load on the engineering branch, together with easing the logistics for provision and maintenance within the Fleet.

The propulsion plant consists of two independent propulsion units each driving its own shaft. In each unit there is an Olympus gas turbine and a Tyne gas turbine which combine in the main gearbox to drive a propeller shaft with its Controllable Pitch Propeller (CPP). The shafts are inward-turning: that is, the port shaft turns clockwise and the starboard shaft anti-clockwise. Neither the gas turbines nor the main gearing can be reversed, so astern power is applied by altering the angle — or pitch — of the propeller. As only one gas turbine can drive each unit at one time, the propulsion system is named 'Combined Gas or Gas' (COGOG) and the arrangement is shown in a diagram.

Olympus

The Rolls-Royce Olympus TM3B (a development of the TMIA) is the larger and more powerful of the engines, developing 25,000 shaft horse power (shp). The two Olympus engines are used when the ship requires high speeds, the maximum speed being in the region of 30kt. The disadvantage of the Olympus is that it has high fuel consumption, using over 6 tons each per hour, and

Left:
Antelope shows her speed and manoeuvrability. Small wonder this class has the reputation of being the sports cars of the Navy. *MoD*

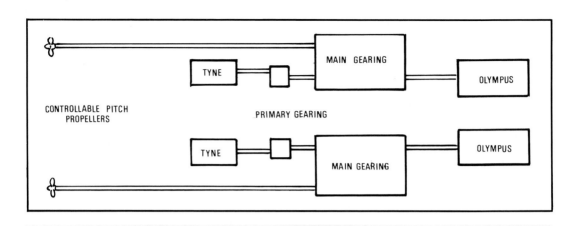

CONTROLLABLE PITCH PROPELLERS

PRIMARY GEARING

TYNE — MAIN GEARING — OLYMPUS

TYNE — MAIN GEARING — OLYMPUS

F170

Left:
Combined Gas or Gas Propulsion Installation.

Below left:
Antelope at sea for Contractor's Sea Trials, the Red Ensign flying. The Type 21s took the new propulsion system of Olympus and Tyne gas turbines to sea for the first time. The two black balls at the port yardarm indicate the ship is 'not under command', no doubt something to do with her engine trials. *Vosper Thornycroft*

Right:
Standing between the two Rolls-Royce Olympus gas turbine modules in the forward Engine Room. The engines are normally controlled from the Ship Control Centre, but can be taken in local control from the position seen. The turbines are out of sight inside the modules, which have their own built-in firefighting system in case of emergency. *Vosper Thornycroft*

Bottom:
Preparing a Tyne engine before its installation. The engine, seen here in the hangar, is slung on a cradle which then guides it on rails down to the after Engine Room. *MoD*

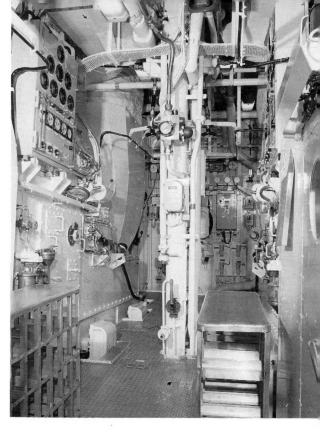

prolonged use cuts down the ship's endurance very noticeably. Acceleration and deceleration are most impressive: a Type 21 can reach its full speed from a position stopped in the water in something like a minute. The feeling of power is exhilarating, and the ability to react to operational requirements and (perhaps more frequently) to the unexpected call for help in a Search and Rescue mission provides the Command with considerable flexibility.

The Olympus main engine comprises a gas generator housed in an acoustic enclosure with a separate single stage power turbine.

The latter is handed for port or starboard shaft, and the overall arrangement allows for the relatively easy removal of the gas generator unit. The fast and simple process of changing gas turbines is one of the advantages. The large space required for its air intake also provides the route for their removal and installation.

Tynes

Whilst the Olympus engines provide the high speeds when required, the Type 21 spends most of its time cruising on the Tyne gas turbines. These are far more economical in fuel usage, and the two engines can combine to give a speed of 18kt, entirely sufficient for most operations. Endurance at such speeds gives ranges in the order of 4,000 nautical miles. One Tyne alone will give a speed of 14kt and a range commensurably increased.

The Rolls-Royce Tyne RMIC gas turbine comprises a Marine Tyne generator with an integral two-stage power turbine, all housed within a single acoustic enclosure. The power turbine drives through a primary single reduction gearbox to the main gearbox. This reduces the higher power turbine speed of the Tyne to that of the Olympus. To achieve contrarotating shafts, the port primary gearbox contains an additional idler gear to reverse the direction of the output shaft.

Initially the Type 21s were fitted with the Tyne RMIA engine, which produces 3,850shp. The Tyne RMIC has, however, been retrofitted in all RN ships, and these engines produce 5,000shp.

All gas turbines have integral systems for fuel, lubrication and support systems. There are local control systems and protection equipment, together with remote control and instrumentation. Separate air intake and exhaust systems are fitted to each turbine, the former providing clean, salt-free combustion air, and having emergency doors. The modules are fitted with fire alarms, together with fire extinguishers which inject a Halon gas.

The engines are normally started and stopped from the *S*hip *C*ontrol *C*entre (SCC), but they can be operated locally. Normally at 10min notice or more, they can, in an

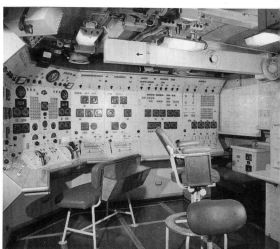

emergency, be started at 2min notice or less. The advantage of near-instant power compared with the 4hr required to raise steam in earlier frigates is obvious.

Gearboxes

The main gearbox is, with the exception of minor detail, the unit which was originally designed for the Type 42.

The gearboxes accept the drive from their respective Olympus/Tyne combination via a torque tube on to a common primary pinion. *S*ynchronous *S*elf *S*hifting (SSS) clutches are fitted on each input to the gearbox, and these automatically engage and disengage the engines according to their speed. The common pinion drives two primary wheels which in turn drive two secondary pinions that drive the main wheel. Propeller thrust bearing pads are located within the gearbox, which is rigidly mounted on the ship's superstructure.

Far left:
The local control panel for the port Tyne engine can be clearly seen with the fitted module firefighting cylinders alongside it to the left. Both Tyne engines and both main gearboxes are housed in this cramped space. *Vosper Thornycroft*

Left:
The Ship Control Centre from where all the machinery is controlled. On the left is the panel which controls the port and starboard engines, either the Olympus or Tyne. Telegraphs and Power Control lever settings are displayed in front of the levers. Further to the right are displays and controls for the fuel supply. Stateboards for each system can be seen, and behind the photographer are the switchboard for the electrical distribution and the Damage Control Centre.
Vosper Thornycroft

Propellers

The torque from the engines is transmitted to the propellers by the main shafting. The five-bladed controllable-pitch propellers are of Stone Manganese Marine's own design. Each propeller hub contains hydraulic activators — a piston and cylinder assembly — and hydraulic power is provided by variable displacement pumps. There are two of these to a shaft, one mechanically driven from the gearbox and the other driven by an electric motor. The hydraulic oil is delivered through oil transfer boxes at the forward end of the main gearbox, and is transferred to the propeller hub via two concentric tubes that run down the centre of the shaft. The propeller pitch is normally automatically controlled by the pitch control lever, known simply as the 'lever', which is situated in the SCC. Unlike other classes with this type of propulsion, there are no levers on the bridge in the Type 21, a cost-saving decision taken at the design stage. Interestingly, there is little perceived disadvantage in this lack of direct bridge control. The lever controls both engine power and propeller pitch: the shaft initially turns on constant revolutions as the pitch increases to its maximum, giving the ship some 10kt, before the shaft revolutions increase until full power is achieved. Gone are the days of steam, when speed was ordered by a number of revolutions. Now it is obtained by a percentage of power, such as 'Set Lever 70'. Fine control is available, but when the telegraph is stopped the pitch is put to zero while the propeller remains turning, thus producing what in effect is a blank plate. This interrupts the flow of water over the rudder directly astern of the propeller and can cause a sheer in an undetermined direction. To overcome this, the wary shiphandler will keep

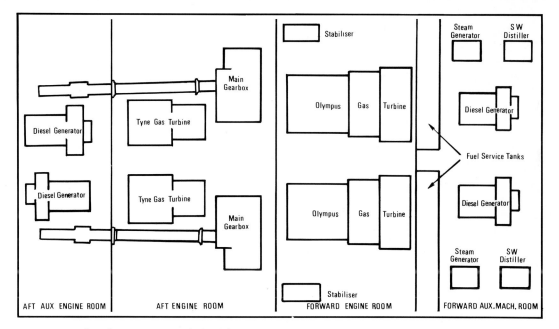

| AFT AUX ENGINE ROOM | AFT ENGINE ROOM | FORWARD ENGINE ROOM | FORWARD AUX.MACH. ROOM |

Above:
Type 21 Machinery Space Layout.

on some ahead or astern pitch whenever possible, to maintain his steerage way.

The gas turbines are situated in two Engine Rooms, the Olympus forward and the Tyne aft. The layout is shown in a diagram which may give a false impression of space. Whilst the Engine Rooms are perhaps less cluttered than in the steam frigates, they still contain a plethora of further equipment: stabilisers, high pressure air compressors, pumps, oil and fuel filters, service tanks and the like, all combining to make these compartments a tangle of pipes and machinery.

Auxiliary Machinery

Flanking the Engine Rooms are two *A*uxiliary *M*achinery *R*ooms (AMR). The forward AMR, known on board as the 'Farm', is a particularly full machinery space crammed with equipment. Two diesel generators dominate the space, but two boilers and two salt water distillers are also bulky. The former supply saturated steam at 100lb/sq in to the distilling plants, the centrifuge heaters and calorifiers, as well as the ventilation and domestic heaters. Both items of equipment are examples of 'bought-in' modules that are typical of the way in which the Type 21 package was quickly brought together. Wherever possible, units are self-contained, pre-assembled under clean factory conditions together with all valves and interconnecting pipework, and can be installed as single packaged units requiring only main piping and electrical connections. This policy proved from the outset to be successful, and

has continued as such through the life of the ships.

The after AMR contains a further two diesel generators, together with an air compressor fuel header tank, and two chilled water plants.

The four diesel generators supply all the electrical power at 440V 60Hz. They are Paxman Ventura 12YJCZ diesels which drive 750kW closed-circuit water-cooled alternators. The primary electrical control console is fitted in the SCC for starting and controlling the generators, setting up and monitoring the main supply system, and controlling the forward and after switchgear units. There are two Switchboard Rooms, one forward and one aft, and each switchboard is further subdivided into sections. The total generating power is well in excess of that required for normal running — one or two would be ample — but the number of generators and the breakdown of the distribution system gives enormous flexibility, which is especially important for the damage control aspect of fighting the ship.

Two other systems vital to the fighting ability and survival of the ship are the Chilled Water System and the Salt Water System. Chilled water is essential for the cooling of the electronic equipment cabinets which serve the ship's sensors, weapons and communications. Without it, the equipment quickly overheats and has to be shut down. Two chilled water

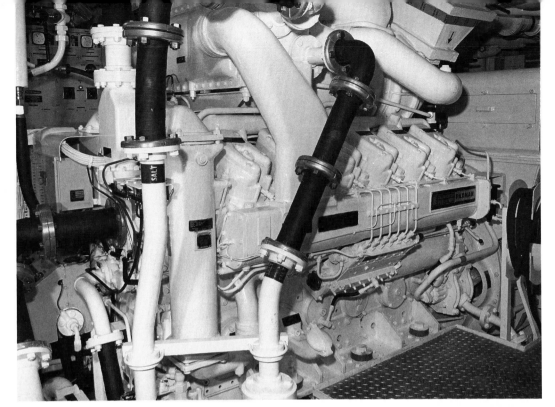

Above:
A small section of the after Auxiliary Machinery Room, showing the starboard diesel generator. The area appears somewhat congested with surrounding pipework, but the machine is more accessible for maintenance than in earlier warships. *Vosper Thornycroft*

plants carry out the required cooling, only one being required at a time. The Salt Water System has a number of purposes. Routinely it is used for the cooling of machinery and for domestic purposes. Perhaps more importantly, it provides emergency services for fire-fighting, magazine spraying, and prewetting, as well as for emergency machinery cooling. The Salt Water System, subdivided into inside and outside machinery space systems, is virtually omnipresent throughout the ship, and as such is inherently complex. Three pumps can serve it, to maintain a pressure of 100lb/sq in. Should all these pumps fail, emergency portable diesel and gas turbine pumps are carried onboard to feed the Salt Water System for emergency firefighting purposes.

The duplication of machinery and the ability to subdivide systems is designed to provide survivability in the face of battle damage. Experience of such damage in the Falklands conflict clearly illustrated the wisdom of this policy, which is standard in all RN warships and is not peculiar to the Type 21.

Right:
To change a diesel generator a removal route is prepared. In this case, the forward Auxiliary Machinery Room has been prepared by removing three decks above it (the deck in the photograph is the Sick Bay Flat). *MoD*

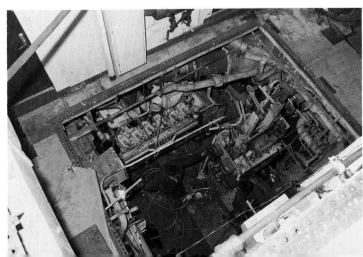

4 A Guided Tour of the Ship

Feeling energetic and got a couple of hours to spare? I'm going to take you on a tour of the ship to give you a feel for it. But watch out — I guarantee that you will have a bruised head and barked shins, for it's a functional ship with not too many allowances made for the crew. No, you needn't change, you'll find it clean throughout and will be able to see even the machinery spaces without getting covered in grease.

Climbing across the brow on to the flight deck, a bit of the old Navy, the long brass plate with the ship's name inscribed on it contrasts with the grey deck, unencumbered with fittings, which acts as the helicopter landing pad. A quick look at the after end of the deck you see the grid, a circular honeycomb of holes into which the helicopter extends its harpoon once it has landed on deck. Surrounding the flight deck are guardrails strung with nets. These lower when at flying stations to be flush with the deck and to provide some safety for the flight deck crew. Just aft of this deck is the miniscule quarterdeck, crowded with bollards, fairleads, a couple of yellow torpedo-like bodies which are 182 sonar anti-torpedo decoys, and a hydraulic winch for their streaming.

Turning forward, you see into the cavern of the hangar, two decks in height and stretching across some three-quarters of the width of the ship. There is a gallery stretching around it, full of helicopter spares which include even rotor blades and an engine. Off the side of the hangar is the air weapons magazine and preparation room, and also the flight's Minute Office and Electronic Maintenance Room. Stepping outside again we go forward into the starboard waist, past the chippy's workshop, into the main access to the ship. The uninitiated may be amused to see the sign 'Stripping Area' upon the door. This is a series of maze-like compartments that allows personnel to enter the so-called 'citadel'. Briefly, the ship is capable of transiting safely an area of nuclear, biological or chemical fallout by closing down inside a citadel kept under positive pressure — in the Type 21 the citadel is most of the ship. Correctly dressed, crew can continue to operate on the upper deck, but need to be stripped and scrubbed before being allowed inside. Hence the 'stripping area'. Such action being unnecessary today, we pass on through into the main passageway, a narrow corridor wide enough only for two

Far left:
Arrow fallen in for entering harbour, Lynx folded but ranged on deck. The flight deck is small, but entirely adequate once the nets are lowered. The grid can be seen in the circle under the helicopter. The hangar is at the forward end of the flight deck with its door rolled down. Above it is the Seacat launcher loaded with two drill missiles. *MoD*

Above left:
The small quarterdeck is not an easy place to work, being so cluttered with fittings. Fuel cans for the Gemini rubber boat are stowed on the starboard quarter, where they can be quickly jettisoned in the event of fire. Beyond them are the two Type 182 torpedo decoy bodies which can be towed astern.
Vosper Thornycroft

Left:
Shot from 500ft above the stern, this photograph of *Alacrity* gives a good impression of the deck layout of the class. The large funnel area contains the exhausts of the Olympus and Tyne gas turbines as well as the diesel generators. No STWS or after 20mm guns are fitted. *MoD*

people to pass. Going forward, you can peer into the two offices on the starboard side, each having a couple of desks, a computer terminal, and bookshelves above lined with manuals and books of reference. This is the Supply and Secretariat empire, the stores office and ship's office, the latter looking after pay and correspondence.

Moving on, past noticeboards cluttered with daily orders, Defence Council orders, sports teams and fixtures, and the normal notices to be expected of any thriving institution, past the Master at Arms' cabin little bigger than your wardrobe, the passageway splits to either side, leading to air conditioning plants and to a Routine Office to starboard and an electrical workshop to port. Forward again into the sickbay flat. At last a wide open uncluttered space. Of course there must be a reason for this — it is the route for removing the diesel generators from three decks below, and this entire deck lifts out. A couple more compartments off this flat include the *Sound Reproduction Equipment* (SRE) Room, which is the heart of the main broadcast, the piped radio and video systems, and then we come to the sickbay.

The design of the sickbay remains generally admired today: it is large, uncluttered, and well

fitted out. A couch serves as an emergency operating table with lights above (but heaven forfend that we should have to use it!), and a couple of bunks adjoin the space, with separate heads and shower. Normally manned only by a Leading Medical Assistant, minor injuries and common infections are his

Above right:
A firefighting team being briefed before entering a compartment on fire. They wear thick wool fearnought suits, breathing apparatus and tank helmets equipped with miners' lights. To fight the fire they will carry hoses pressurised with sea water.

Right:
View from the eyes of the ship: the 4.5in gun and Exocet missiles can clearly be seen. The team is preparing to replenish fuel by taking a hose from a tanker through the roller fairleads (seen on the left-hand side of the photograph) and then connecting it to the hose ranged on the forecastle.
MoD

everyday business. When he produces his dental valise it is time to escape. We are now in the Wardroom flat area, moving up the port side between cabins on either hand. There are 12 in all, two of which are double berths. The officers' cabins are about the size of a railway compartment. Their bunks fold away in the daytime to form a seat and the cabin doubles as their office, crammed with safes, filing systems, and with a wardrobe and chest of drawers for personal effects. Amidst these cabins is the Wardroom itself, a magnificent area which is well furnished and of comfortable proportions. It is the envy of many other classes of warships — perhaps the private design had something to do with it! Here the officers relax and take their meals, which are cooked in a small galley just forward of the Wardroom.

We are in the forward part of the ship now, and step out of the Wardroom flat on to the forecastle, dominated by the gun turret. Looking up to the deck above, you see the four Exocet launchers, pointing inwards and rather pigeon-toed. Rather than climb the vertical ladder up to them, we will go back inside to the crossroads just by the galley. A glance into the Captain's cabin shows that he is spoilt with outstanding accommodation — his own bath-

room and heads, a small sleeping cabin, and a day-cabin nearly 15ft square. Of course this doubles as his office too, but he often entertains here, and he takes all his meals at the dining table.

Let us descend a deck on to 1 deck, and move forward, peering down into some of the spaces below us. A small bulkhead door right forward lets us into the large compartment full of spare gear, the huge drum holding the plaited tow rope, and a number of berthing hawsers. There is a 15ft vertical ladder up to the escape hatch on the forecastle. Back through the small door a notice states that it should be clipped shut at all times, reminding us that this is the specially strengthened collision bulkhead. The capstan motor dominates the next space, but there is a small store off it, and a black dingy compartment beneath it which is the cable locker.

Aft of here we pass through the forward Damage Control Base, equipped with state-boards, which are maps and diagrams of the ship from which damage control can be planned and plotted. Another naval store to one side and below, full of brightly polished aluminium drawers and shelves containing thousands of articles. Thence into the gunbay flat with magazine and stores below it, and the

Left:
An unusual view, taken from the top of the bridge roof, looking down on to the Exocet deck. The missiles come self-contained in boxes which are connected to ramps. The missile is not reloadable, so once expended the container has to be replaced. You can see the ramps and electrical cabling before the missile containers are loaded.
Vosper Thornycroft

circular gunbay — restricted to us, but we'll peer into it — containing some ready-use ammunition and the impressive array of the feed ring, looking not too dissimilar to a bottling factory. Should the maintainer be there to show you the system in action, you might be somewhat taken aback by the alarming noise of the rounds being moved around by the hydraulic system. A look through the door opposite reveals a very different compartment, one with only a quiet hum of bank upon bank of electronic panels. This is the sonar instrument space, and these are the Type 184 sonar amplifiers, generating a great deal of heat which is then removed by chilled water.

Above:
The midships section of *Active*, soon after she was built. The 20mm Oerlikon cannon are on the bridge wings with the 2in rocket launchers further aft. The 'main roof' aerial is slung between yards on the fore and mainmasts. *Vosper Thornycroft*

Below left:
A senior rates mess, with trophy cabinet in far bulkhead. Senior rates sleep in separate three berth cabins located away from this mess. *MoD*

Below:
With a saloon-type atmosphere, this junior rates mess deck is home for nearly 50 sailors. The mess square, a recreational space is in the centre with bunk spaces around the outside of the compartment. One such space containing three bunks and individual lockers can just be seen beyond the drawn back curtain. *MoD*

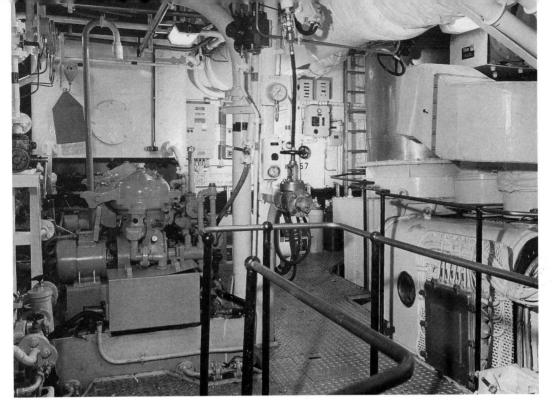

Above:
The After Engine Room, showing one small part of it — the starboard after end. There are two main lubrication oil purifying units here on the left, with the associated drain tank. To the right is the starboard Tyne gas turbine, within the container, and its inlet trunking leading down from above.
Vosper Thornycroft

Stepping aft into the next section, we enter the accommodation area of the ship. We won't look down into the 184 sonar space — it's large and empty, and all you would see is the raft at the bottom under which the transducer is slung. Senior Ratings' cabins flank the outboard side of this section. Three to a cabin, these are small but comfortable, with a homely atmosphere enhanced by photographs of the family. For relaxation there are the Warrant and Chief Petty Officers' Mess and the Petty Officers' Mess. Both have a bar set in the corner with bench seats around the outside, and a TV set fixed into the bulkhead. Each mess is home for some 25 men, so life can be cramped but friendly! The Junior Ratings have messdecks: one small one on this deck with 25 living there, and two larger ones (about 30ft by 40ft) with accommodation for nearly 50 in each. In each mess there is a recreational space, called the Mess Square, flanked by bench seats with sleeping berths around the

outside of the square. These take the form of three or four-bunk semi-cabins, with small individual lockers and a tiny wardrobe — certainly very cramped, but nevertheless a very big advance on accommodation standards in previous classes, and still thought to be amongst the best in the RN. The mess itself is brightly lit, and cheerfully decorated with trophies from around the world, the inevitable but tasteful pin-ups, and probably with a small bar with a fridge containing their cans of beer, issued on a daily basis at three cans per man. These mess decks are on the waterline, and below them are fuel tanks and a small Gyro Compass Room.

We are nearly halfway aft now, as we pass through another bulkhead door. A switchboard is to starboard, and a tiny laundry to port, with a massive pile of washing, known as dhobying, awaiting the enthusiastic attention of the Chinese laundrymen on contract from Hong Kong. Senior and Junior Rates' bathrooms and heads flank the flat, in which there is set a hatch which leads down into the forward Auxiliary Engine Room. We'll go down, but first must put on ear defenders, for there is a diesel generator running, and making quite a racket. As we climb down the ladder we enter an entirely different world — a large compartment, but crammed full of machinery, dials, pipes, valves; a seeming tangle of incom-

prehensible equipment. Another chapter describes the equipment and its use, but it would not fully forewarn the visitor as to the atmosphere of the space. There is room to walk around the machinery on narrow deck-plates and up and down small ladders, but as you bump your head at least twice it is small wonder that you are indicating (I can't hear what you say) that we should go back up.

That was only the first of the four machinery spaces. The next one we approach through one of the narrowest passageways of the ship, between the Olympus engine intakes and exhausts. Passing a considerable amount of machinery again, the air conditioning plants, we climb down into the forward Engine Room. Less cramped than the last, this space is dominated by the two enormous Olympus modules, huge white boxes with remarkably few appendages, connected to the outside world by their large intakes and exhaust pipes. There's a fair amount of machinery scattered around the edge of the compartment, but it's not too bad. Out we go, up and down into the after Engine Room — a similar-looking compartment, although with even more equipment. Another two large engine modules, less than half the size of the Olympus, these contain the Tynes, and outboard of these are the large blue metallic covers to the main gearboxes, from which you can see the propeller shafts leading aft. These are nearly 2ft in diameter, and you can follow them below the deckplates to the after bulkhead. A criss-cross of pipes fills the compartment, connecting fuel filters and pumps and carrying lubricating oil around the compartment. In comparison, the after Auxiliary Machinery Room is pretty small, but as crowded as any other by the two diesel engines side by side, flanked by complicated-looking chilled water plants, and with an HP air compressor hissing in the starboard after corner. With some relief we leave the machinery spaces, and with an increased respect for the men who work down there and understand the entire workings of it all.

We have got two Technical Offices to glance into, though there is nothing beyond a couple of desks, computer screens to help the search for stores, a mass of reference books, and the microfilm system that is meant to have replaced them. Planned maintenance, and indeed emergency repairs, are co-ordinated from these offices; and round the corner is a small workshop with a lathe, drills and so on to give onboard facility for repairs. Opposite are warning signs that the Seacat magazine is beyond a locked watertight door.

Nearly aft now on 1 deck, we go into the Ship Control Centre (SCC) to be met by the watchkeepers. This compartment is manned both at sea and in harbour, and has hundreds of dials set into control panels showing the state of all the onboard machinery. A switchboard in one corner shows the electrical state, and a series of fire alarm systems are monitored from here. The SCC doubles as the Damage Control Headquarters, and there is a comprehensive set of stateboards showing the detailed layout of the ship and its systems. A bank of switches and telephones give the correct impression that this compartment is the hub of communication to all parts of the ship.

On, past the NAAFI shop with its counter laden with nutty and goffers (sweets and soft drinks), we come to the main galley and dining halls. These are situated immediately under the flight deck and above the propellers, which can make them noisy places at sea during operations. A stainless steel serving counter fronts the galley, framing the chefs preparing and serving the food beyond. To feed 180 ratings there is a cafeteria system of self-service from the choice of up to five selections of main course. Senior and Junior Ratings eat separately, with tables to seat about a third at a

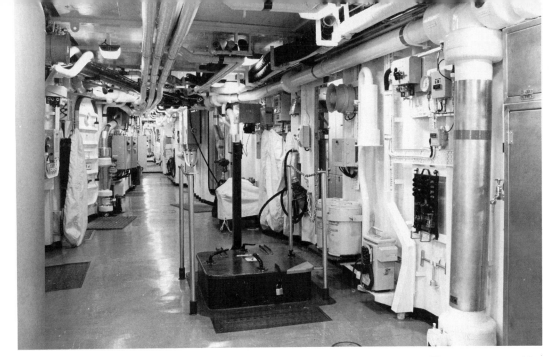

time. The scullery is small for the numbers, but a mammoth-sized dishwasher takes most of the strain off the potwash, manned by members of the ship's company who rotate through the communal party. You cannot fail to notice the red lockers filling the sides of the dining hall, and the wooden timber struts lashed above. This space serves as the after Damage Control section base, and has a considerable amount of emergency equipment stowed away. Breathing apparatus, scattered throughout the ship for instant use, is also stowed here. There are more DC stateboards and communications for the teams. At the other end of the scale, this same dining hall serves also as the ship's library with a large enclosed set of shelves. Books are updated on a monthly basis and are particularly varied.

We can descend beneath the galley to look at the caterer's storerooms. These are served by a lift from the upper deck — a breakthrough in design to save effort in storing ship, but a hazardous system for the unwary operator. Three walk-in refrigerators or cold rooms contain a mass of frozen food and fresh vegetables, and these are kept cool by the adjacent refrigeration machinery. Food for three months plus can be stored, to give the ship's company a varied and healthy diet over a protracted period.

Mounting the ladder, we move aft into the final section of the ship. A small paintshop and a Sonar 182 Winch Room on this deck, and two hatches down, one to storerooms and the avcat pump space, and the other into the tiller flat. We'll go down the latter, into a compartment where we have to bend double. Here are two large rudder heads connecting with the

Top:
The passageway of 2 deck, looking forward from outside the Ship Control Centre. The hatch leads down to the after Auxiliary Machinery Room. The large pipe on the right of the photograph carries salt water, primarily for firefighting, while smaller pipes carry chilled water for cooling the electronics of the weapon systems.
Vosper Thornycroft

Right:
Inside the Junior Ratings' Dining Hall a party is being given to disadvantaged children during a port visit. The Dining Hall is somewhat sparse, and serves as a Damage Control Base as well. Pipes and cables run overhead and down the bulkheads to serve the surrounding compartments. *MoD*

Above:
A view of the Operations Room in harbour with the lights on. The large desk-like consoles are the Decca display units with a horizontal radar picture, which will be used by two people sitting in the chairs on either side. Complex internal and external communications are mounted alongside and above the radar. The ladder to the bridge can just be seen on the extreme right.
Vosper Thornycroft

Above right:
The large bridge has an excellent view and plenty of space. The helmsman sits in the high chair on the left of the photograph, steering with the two-handed control in front of him. Engine telegraphs and engine power settings are also on his panel. Unlike other gas turbine ships, the engines cannot be controlled directly from the bridge. Standing centrally on the bridge is the pelorus, with its gyro repeater, and beyond is the Captain's chair and the communications desk.
Vosper Thornycroft

complicated steering mechanism. Creeping round and over all this we get a feel for the massive machinery which steers the ship with such precision. There is a position here for a quartermaster to take over the steering in an emergency, with communications direct to the bridge. We'll escape another way and ascend the vertical ladder through a tiny escape hatch on to the quarterdeck.

Well — that's 1 deck and below. Time is running out, so we cross the flight deck again and climb up the ladder to 01 deck, past the triple torpedo tubes, looking only briefly up at the Seacat launcher and director. Under the whaler we re-enter the citadel and another narrow passageway. We could go aft and look at the Seacat Control Room, and indeed climb into the large space of the hollow funnel, but you are looking anxiously at your watch! Forward we go to find the radio equipment rooms and Main Communication Office to port. We are not allowed to go in there, but past the Electrical Maintenance Room we can

peer into the Radar Office, where we find the guts of the search radars. Black boxes indeed, and not too much to see apart from a few waveguides to take the pulses to and from the aerials. The Computer Room sounds more interesting, being the heart of the action information and weaponry systems. But when you see it, just two grey cabinets the size of a large wardrobe — how disappointing.

We step through a door into the Operations Room, and you gasp in surprise. Having set it up for you as you would find it at sea, it appears pitch black, and only gradually can you make out glowing cathode ray tubes with radar and sonar pictures on them; a considerable number of dials, speakers, knobs and switches; display boards with meaningless codes, duties, arrows and the like. It looks like NASA's space control. You walk around the consoles seeing blips, computer readouts and flashing lights, and hearing squawking radios and active loudspeakers. You question the fact that anyone could understand and work in this environment, and climb the ladder on to the bridge.

Sanity returns: you can see out of the windows, take in the more obvious features of a compass, chart table, communications panels, and just one radar screen. You ask where the ship's wheel is, but find that it has always been in the form that is more akin to an aircraft's control. At least you recognise the small telegraph with Stop, Slow, Half and Full Ahead on it. Perhaps the most striking aspect of the bridge is its size, for it stretches virtually the width of the ship and has a magnificent all-round view. Exhausted, you sink into the Captain's chair, not unlike a dentist's chair. We have finished our tour. When I tell you that we have visited less than half the compartments onboard you groan, and accept that these ships are very much more complicated than you ever realised. You cannot fail to be impressed.

5 Type 21s at Work

What does a warship do? A common question that must be answered at length. Type 21 frigates have exceptionally busy programmes that reflect the work-rate of the Royal Navy today. They participate fully in the entire range of activities, and have deservedly earned the reputation of being the work-horses of the 1980s.

Operational Commitments

Britain has a long-standing commitment to provide warships to NATO in the event of tension or hostilities, and the Type 21 is earmarked for the Eastern Atlantic area. In peacetime there are a number of operational commitments for the Royal Navy in pursuance

Below:
Amazon breaks away from RFA Bayleaf after carrying out a station-keeping exercise. Shiphandling experience is given to the junior bridge watchkeepers at every opportunity. *MoD*

of foreign policy. These include the South Atlantic, for the defence of the Falkland Islands, and the West Indies as part of the British forces supporting Belize. Type 21s are frequently the class chosen for fulfilling both these duties, and they can expect to deploy to these areas for some five months every two years or so. The Armilla patrol in the Gulf has been in progress for a number of years, and the class has been well represented during that time. As tension has increased and missile attacks on ships become almost commonplace, so there has been a tendency to detail either Seadart- or Seawolf-armed ships to the area. However, this had not been exclusively so, and HMS *Active* saw a full deployment there in 1987.

Other standing commitments that the Type 21 becomes involved with are as the RN representative in the NATO forces: the *Standing Naval Force Atlantic* (STANAVFORLANT),

Above:
**Dwarfed by a Shell tanker,
Active gives protection as a
close escort whilst passing
through the Straits of Hormuz
into the Gulf. *Active* carried
out an Armilla patrol during
the recent heightened tension,
but nearly all of the class have
participated in the patrol.**
MoD

Left:
**One of four ships of the 'Naval
on Call Force Mediterranean',
Amazon lies alongside the
Turkish destroyer *Savastepe*.
Astern are the USA destroyer
Richard E. Byrd and the Italian
frigate *Perseo*. They had just
completed taking part in
Exercise 'Opengate' and were
visiting Palma, Mallorca. The
NATO flag flies on their
starboard yardarms.** *MoD*

and the *Naval On Call Force Med*iterranean
(NAVOCFORMED), which activates for a six-
week period twice a year.

Exercises

To be effective in their roles, warships must
exercise frequently to maintain their operational effectiveness. Naval exercises vary in
complexity and length, and can involve a
couple of units or vast numbers of warships,
merchantmen, aircraft, and even armies
ashore. The latter type tend to be major NATO
exercises, which can last for a month and can
cover the whole Atlantic from the American
coastline to North Cape. It is usual for Type 21s
to take part in these, exercising in their role as
escorts for merchantmen, replenishment ships
or carrier groups. The escorting of amphibious

reinforcements for Norway is also exercised on
a frequent basis.

National exercises take place from time to
time along with exercises on a bi-national
basis outside the NATO organisation. All these
work to prove and improve tactics and
weapons, and further the deterrent role of the
armed services.

Surveillance

Another vital duty for the Navy is the
surveillance of foreign navies operating within
NATO areas of interest. Ships have the right of
passage on the high seas, and intelligence-
gathering by surface ships, including warships,
special intelligence vessels, merchantmen and
also submarines is a daily event. Soviet ships
are frequently to be found around the North

Above:
Regular exercises are carried out by Type 21s in Norwegian waters. The RN has a major role to play in amphibious operations in these northern seas. Here, anchor ready for letting go, *Ambuscade* navigates through the leads.
MoD

Right:
Leaving harbour manoeuvres, *Active* sails in company with two Type 42 destroyers for exercises. Showing her all-grey colour scheme, she has had her pennant number and flight deck identification initials painted out. *MoD*

Atlantic, and the Type 21 frigate is amongst those Allied warships that are tasked to keep an eye on them.

Training and Trials

A considerable amount of the training of officers and ratings in the Royal Navy is carried out at sea, normally for a week at a time. Whilst there used to be a squadron of frigates based at Portland purely for this task, the load is now spread across the Fleet, and the Type 21s are frequently used. The training of Principal Warfare Officers in gunnery and anti-submarine warfare, of Lynx Pilots in deck landings, of Officers of the Watch in coastal navigation, and of Operations Department Ratings in basic operation procedures, are typical examples of the variety of training tasks undertaken by these ships.

Another activity which fills the sea programme is involvement in Fleet Trials, trying

Top:
Inside Gibraltar harbour with her anchor ready for letting go, *Ambuscade* sails ahead of a 'County' class guided missile destroyer. Seen in pre-Exocet days, the 3in Chaff Launchers are still mounted forward of the bridge, *MoD*

Left:
***Avenger* on surveillance operations. Here she is in company with the Russian helicopter carrier *Moskva*. She is wearing the broad black band of the Leader of her Squadron, designated by the number 4. The forward 912 tracker is trained on the Russian ship, not transmitting on radar but probably recording it on its video camera.** *MoD*

Left:
Chasing another Russian. *Avenger* closes on a 'Kresta 2' cruiser with its highly distinctive silhouette. The photograph is taken from the ship's helicopter, which is returning to 'mother' having taken a series of photographs of the 'Kresta'. *MoD*

Right:
A light jackstay transfer from one ship to another. A good seamanship evolution, the tensioning of the jackstay and heaving in of the traveller block is done entirely by hand while the ships steam alongside each other at some 80ft apart. *MoD*

Bottom:
***Active* leaves Gibraltar, a frequent base for Type 21 frigates whilst training Principal Warfare Officers in live firings of the 4.5in gun.** *MoD*

out new equipment specially fitted to the ship for the trial, or being used as a target for another unit. Not the most exciting of programmes, trials at sea are a necessary part of the research programme for weapons and sensors being developed by the Admiralty Research Establishment and private contractors.

Operational Sea Training

A warship cannot become instantly operationally effective after it has been built or refitted: rather, there is a process to bring it up to speed. The process starts at HMS *Dryad*, near Portsmouth, where an Operations Room crew goes for Command Team Training, manning Ops Room simulators and going through tactical seminars where mistakes can be made and lessons learnt. There is a Type 21 'model' incorporated to give a most realistic feeling for the team. Sonar operators train on the appropriate sonar simulators, and the Marine Engineering Department will train its team of simulators at HMS *Sultan* in Gosport.

Once at sea the ship will shake itself down before going to Portland to come under the supervision of Flag Officer Sea Training for a period of highly intensive training that can vary

Above right:
Warships never know when they might be called upon to take another ship in tow, so this is an evolution that is practised every few months. Here *Amazon* **prepares to be taken in tow.** *MoD*

Right:
Reversing the role, a tow rope is passed across to *Manchester.* **The towing hawser is an extremely strong braided rope that could tow this ship at speeds of up to 10kt.** *MoD*

Below:
Replenishing fuel by the abeam method. The Type 21 and 'Leander' frigates are dwarfed by the 'O' class tanker. *MoD*

Above:
Tanker's view of *Amazon* connecting up the fuel hose. *MoD*

Below:
In rough weather, when it may not be possible to maintain station alongside a tanker, ships can take fuel by the astern method. Note the two balls with a diamond in between, signalling that the frigate is conducting special operations and is unable to manoeuvre. *MoD*

from four to six weeks. Every variety of exercise that can be imagined is carried out under the close eye of the staff 'sea riders', who are there to give detailed and constructive criticism in order to raise standards. Gunnery and missile firings take place; hours of flying include helicopter emergencies; submarines are hunted; navigational training practices for narrow channels and thick fog. Replenishments, tows, boardings, fires, floods and even disaster-relief exercises fill the days and nights to push the ship's company to find their limitations. Whilst this goes on the stores and galleys come under close scrutiny, paperwork is checked, and the whole organisation is given a thorough going-through.

Visits

'We joined the Navy to see the world, and what did we see? . . .' The image of the Royal Navy being spread around the world in often sun-soaked locations is to a degree outdated, but the role of 'showing the flag' is still deemed to be a significant one. Type 21s have travelled the world throughout their existence, and have proved their worth on countless occasions. Deployments to the West Indies, South Atlantic and Mediterranean have already been mentioned, but the class has been well represented also in deployments to the Far East. Lately HMS *Amazon* was part of a round-the-world deployment consisting of a group of four warships and three Royal Fleet Auxiliaries that visited 17 countries in nine months during

A magnificent spectacle that draws the crowds. *Active* shows off her fine lines by floodlighting. The lights are mounted on the ends of the booms that are suspended off the ship's side, seen here as small black dots at the deck level. *MoD*

Above:
In close formation at the start of a worldwide deployment, *Amazon* manoeuvres with *Manchester*, *Beaver* and *Southampton*. *MoD*

Left:
Alacrity visits Grand Harbour, Valletta, Malta. Standing in the foreground is a dghaisa, a Maltese passenger boat which is propelled by one or two men who stand and push the oars rather than sit and pull them. *MoD*

1986. (*Amazon's* visits included Venezuela, the USA, Canada, Hawaii, China, Hong Kong, Thailand, Singapore, Malaysia, Indonesia, Australia, Mauritius, Tanzania, Jordan, and Gibraltar.) Not typical of British deployments, there was nevertheless both an operational and diplomatic background to 'Global 86'. A considerable amount of the time was spent exercising with friendly nations and allies around the world. The opportunity was frequently taken to further the UK defence industrial base by giving sales days for salesmen to demonstrate their equipment in a realistic environment, with the Royal Navy acting as 'honest brokers'.

Above all, however, 'showing the flag' involves the spreading of goodwill at all levels, and a furthering of understanding between groups of peoples of different nations. The benefits are hard to quantify, and cannot normally be seen to be of financial profit, but that goodwill is generated during these visits is undoubtedly the case. This needs to be observed at first hand to be understood, but letters of appreciation afterwards from the local community and the British Diplomatic Corps make the successes clear, and invitations to return are the norm.

It might be assumed that a port visit sees little more than a few mind-blowing runs-ashore for the crew. Rest and recreation certainly form a part of the visit, and an opportunity to visit a new district or country. The work-load nevertheless is very high. On arrival alongside the Captain will depart on official calls on the local dignitaries and military commanders, whilst the ship's company squares away the ship to prepare it for visitors. The calls are followed by return calls onboard, and perhaps a lunch party in the Captain's cabin for seven guests. Presidents, Governors, Admirals, Lord Mayors, Harbour-masters, Judges have all graced, with many others, the Type 21s. Lunch over, there is more official business to be done before the evening's official reception, when some hundred guests from the local community will come aboard to be entertained to drinks and small eats by the ship's officers. The party is held as often as not on the flight deck under a red and white striped awning, and perhaps with a decorative pond and fountain rigged by the officers under training.

Ships are normally opened to visitors for one or two afternoons during the visit, when the public can wander around looking at displays and talking to the ship's company. Perhaps 50 will visit, but it is more likely that numbers will run into thousands. Private tours for schools and other organisations will take place on a daily basis.

Meanwhile, sporting fixtures will be taking place against local teams. Receptions ashore may be attended, and the social exchange continues. It is usual for children from a special home or hospital to be invited onboard for a party, run by volunteers, with jellies, cakes, games and cartoons to entertain them. Other volunteers may go to assist some local charity in painting or repairing their property. And so it goes on, with a full programme to occupy many on board.

Such visits are not confined to overseas, for it is common for all warships to visit a UK port away from their home base at least once a year, perhaps for four days or so. The visit programme takes much the same form as that just described. 'Meet the Navy' visits are seen as an important way of showing the Royal Navy to the taxpayer, who has a vested interest in the Service; they also act as an excellent method of recruitment. Each frigate has a town which has adopted it, and with which it will keep special ties. These also are made with one or two schools, Sea Cadet groups, local charities and so on. These affiliations are prized by the ships: a list of those belonging to Type 21 frigates can be found in the appendices at the back of this book.

Home Port Time

Type 21s are based at Devonport, Plymouth, and on completion of their exercises and deployments it is there that they head for their leave and maintenance periods. The broad aim is to have some 40% of the ship's operational life in her home port, but few of the ships' companies would say that it seems that much!

Leave entitlement accounts for six weeks in the year if operations permit, but even then a quarter of the ship's company will remain onboard as the 'Duty Party' to look after the security of the ship and to act as a Fire and Emergency Party.

Maintenance periods vary greatly in content and length according to the phase of the ship's operational life. Refits can last a year, and involve a major overhaul of all items of the ship, providing a nearly-new warship at the end of it. A lesser period, but one still incorporating a great deal of work, is a DED (Docking and Essential Defects), which can last three or four months. In effect this is a mini

refit, with the majority of the work being done by the recently-privatised Dockyard in Devonport. Between DEDs come Assisted Maintenance Periods (AMP), and Self Maintenance Periods (SMP). During these, the RN undertakes nearly all the work, and local Fleet Maintenance Groups come onboard to assist with the maintenance load.

The time alongside is one of great activity for the ship's company. They share a considerable load of the maintenance, carry out all their normal duties, and maintain the cleanliness of the ship. They also undertake a massive training programme to further their skills. Professional advancement courses, leadership, first aid and firefighting courses, boarding party and internal security exercises, command team and marine engineering training on simulators, ships' divers' courses, tactical courses . . . the list goes on.

It is not all hard work, however. Sport plays a large part in a ship's life, and there are competitions in all the major sports and a number of minor ones too. Other recreational pursuits such as skiing, parachuting, canoeing, sailing and hill-walking are also available and popular with some. One feature for the Type 21s is a regular Olympiad sports afternoon when those of the class in harbour compete between themselves in a variety of sports for a Squadron Cup.

Right:
Entering an enclosed dry dock, *Amazon* prepares for refit in the massive frigate complex at Devonport. She is seen here in her pre-Exocet appearance, the box-like fittings on 01 deck in front of the bridge being 3in rocket lockers. *MoD*

6 But it's not all Work

The previous chapter describes the high work-load of the ship's company, but it would be incorrect to form the impression of 'all work and no play'. One of the most enjoyable aspects of life onboard a warship is the close-knit community, and the inter-mess activity and friendly competition. 'Mess life' is a foundation stone of life at sea.

The working day cannot be said to end at any particular time, in that there will always be at least a quarter of the crew closed up on watch, and whilst on exercise the proportion will be increased to over a half. Even when on passage during a quiet phase of the programme the period between 'secure' at tea-time and dusk will be interspersed with 'man overboard' exercises, where a dummy is dropped into the sea and the ship has to manoeuvre to recover it by swimmer or seaboat, or perhaps with steering gear 'failures', during which the primary steering machinery is taken out, and alternative means have to be employed. These exercises are done against the clock, to train and test the watchkeepers in instant reactions. Machinery breakdowns will be practised, where the Marine Engineering Department will stage a succession of malfunctioning systems for the training of their team. Meanwhile, it is quite normal for the Flight to be embarked on FLYEX, which will often be after dark. The team have to complete a set number of hours of night flying each month.

Below:
Ambuscade enters Taranto harbour after exercising with NATO navies. She certainly pulls in the crowds. *MoD*

Right:
Another use for the flightdeck! Here *Ambuscade* is playing in fine conditions. The spring securing the ball can be seen across the net.
MoD

Personal advancement is high on the list of priorities onboard, and to this end there will be frequent lessons given by the officers and senior ratings. These will be both professional, to prepare the individual for promotion exams for the next rate, and educational. The latter may be at a basic level, the Navy having its own mathematics and English tests to ensure that ratings have an adequate level of knowledge for advancement to Leading Hand or above, or at 'O' level and sometimes beyond. It is quite normal for several members of a ship's company to be students of the Open University.

With all this going on, it is difficult to say when relaxation starts! It is not unusual to have an hour or so of sports in the Dog Watches (first Dogwatch 16.00-18.00; last Dogwatch 18.00-20.00), and this will take place on the pitch otherwise known as the Flight Deck. Obviously not compatible with flying operations, a degree of rivalry between the Sports Officer and Flight Commander has been known. The weather, naturally, also has a considerable influence on the activity. Flight deck sports provide an opportunity to get some fresh air and a run-around together with inter-mess competitions. Deck hockey is popular, and a plentiful supply of home-made pucks are required to replace those lost overboard. Volley-ball and cricket are both played, the ball being tied to a piece of string!

At sea over a weekend it would be usual to see a sports afternoon, with competitions involving the sports just mentioned or even an inter-mess Olympiad. This will see a host of activities of the 'It's A Knockout' variety, designed to get the maximum numbers of teams competing at the same time.

Apart from team games there are normally the daily sessions of keep-fit exercises, well attended by the ship's company, and these can be fitted easily into the space available. If the flight deck cannot be used, then the signal deck is an alternative venue – though the thumping of the deck during various sprints and step-ups can be rather off-putting to those below in the Operations Room. Weight-lifting is a popular sport; a weight-training bench is commonly in use on the signal deck, and there is a small gym in the 'fridge flat that can be used in virtually any weather.

Right:
Sailors of any age and rank appear capable of standing up and making a fool of themselves! A long period at sea often sees an evening of entertainment in the form of skits and singing. The hangar or, as in this case, the flight deck make a very good venue for what is normally an excellent evening's entertainment. *MoD*

Whilst the ship's company is deployed away from home for long periods and with prolonged sea-time, there is time to find other activities to bring the men together and into the fresh air. Barbecues are feasible, and may be the prelude to either a ship's entertainment (known as a 'Sod's Opera'), where individuals or groups show off their prowess in singing or comic skits, or perhaps a night at the races. Horse racing is a popular activity: the flight deck is marked out as a racecourse, six different-colour horses are auctioned and then raced according to the throw of dice. Much excitement and merriment ensues, and a fair amount of money can be raised for the ship's charity. Entertainments vary from ship to ship, but another large fund-raiser for charity seen from time to time is a fair, with a multitude of stalls including coconut shies and Aunt Sallies. A deployment away from the UK can result in a thousand pounds or more being collected by such events.

These are all antics to be had on the upper deck, but the main recreational activities centre around the mess decks in the evening. Videos have crept into each mess, and each ship has a centralised CCTV system – particularly novel features when the Type 21 was first at sea. Films, either on video or 16mm, are shown most evenings from a library provided by the

Left:
Crossing the Equator is the time that King Neptune reigns. Regardless of rank all are drawn forward for trial and subsequent ducking in a pool constructed on the flightdeck. *MoD*

Below:
Not a common activity, but certainly enormous fun. Fulfilling a life-long ambition, the author water-skis across the Equator, 80 miles off the coast of East Africa. *MoD*

RN Film Corporation. There is a danger that ship's companies as a whole become square-eyed, and that mess life is on the decline, but there remain a host of mess-deck games that are popular. 'Uckers' is an old-time favourite, similar to Ludo, but with cut-throat tactics and the Navy's own rules. Crib and dominoes bear more resemblance to their civilian counterparts as do the various common card games. A dartboard appears occasionally – the billiard table never! Games may be played between messmates, or in inter-mess competitions.

Yet another frequent feature is a quiz given over the ship's broadcast system to the messes. Made up on board or cribbed from books, the questions are traditionally asked by the Leading Physical Training rating, or the Padre if he is embarked. More adventurous ships may put on a series of 'Call My Bluff' or other team games from television, and these will normally be staged in the Junior Rates' Dining Hall.

Privacy onboard is hard to come by and missed by many. The design of the mess decks of the Type 21 is such that an activity can take place in the mess square whilst the bunk spaces offer a degree of quiet for the individual. One of the most important features of shipboard life is mail, the fundamental link with home and loved ones whilst away. Every opportunity is taken to land and receive mail, though it may have to take somewhat circuitous routes, courtesy of *British Forces Post Office* (BFPO), foreign postal services and the British diplomatic channels. Nothing is worse than sailing from a foreign port knowing that mailbags are sitting in a local airport, unobtainable because of a national bank holiday or some such reason. Mail is one of the fundamental factors affecting morale when ships operate away from home.

It may be imagined that alcohol is an important morale booster, but because of the entire crew's close proximity to their work and the requirement to be at very short notice to close up with action or emergency, there is no place for any form of over-indulgence. The days of 'up spirits' and the issue of pusser's rum were never seen by the Type 21 companies, but the abolition of the tot did see the introduction of a spirit allowance for senior ratings. They are now permitted a couple of measures of spirits should they wish, in addition to a less rationed quantity of beer. Junior ratings are limited to four cans of beer a day, whilst the officers' consumption is left to their own discretion. Drunkenness onboard is exceptionally rare and is extremely severely punished, but self-discipline in the matter is the most important factor, with the onus being put on the individual to act responsibly.

Time in harbour takes a different form. The previous chapter describes the official business to be done alongside, both at home and abroad. Further to all that, a Duty Part of a Watch, consisting of some 25 men will look after the security and safety of the ship. After working hours, which abroad may be shorter than normal, the remainder of the ship's company may step ashore. Sightseeing and shopping (perhaps to buy 'rabbits', a time-honoured word to describe the sailor's presents bought abroad as souvenir gifts for his return), together with sport, form the day's activities. There may be a visit to the local beach if it is the right time of the year. Keeping fit continues to be important to many individuals, and the opportunity to use terra firma for jogging is irresistible to many. Come the evening, a meal and a quiet drink ashore may attract the older members, whilst a night on the town beckons the lads.

7 Helicopter Operations

Ever since the Type 12 frigate was modified to take a helicopter in the late 1960s, the role of the Fleet Air Arm has been assured. All warships of frigate size and above have been equipped to carry a helicopter, first the Wasp and later the Lynx.

The helicopter is a vital asset to a frigate, extending the horizons and giving the ability to attack the enemy at great ranges. Its speed and

Below:
A Wasp AS Mk 1 lands on *Antelope*. Type 21s were designed to carry the Lynx, but had to make do with the Wasp until the Lynx became operational. Note the absence of the grid. *MoD*

versatility are major attributes which, combined with the frigate's ability to sustain prolonged operations, gives a capability far in excess of that of earlier frigates. The major roles of the helicopter are in reconnaissance, anti-submarine and anti-surface warfare, and Search and Rescue.

Although the Type 21s were designed from the outset to carry the Lynx, the early commissions saw the older Wasp embarked, the Lynx not being ready for operational service. The Westland Wasp AS Mk 1 had been operational since the early 1960s. Although it gave sterling service, it was limited by being single-engined and radarless. It was relatively

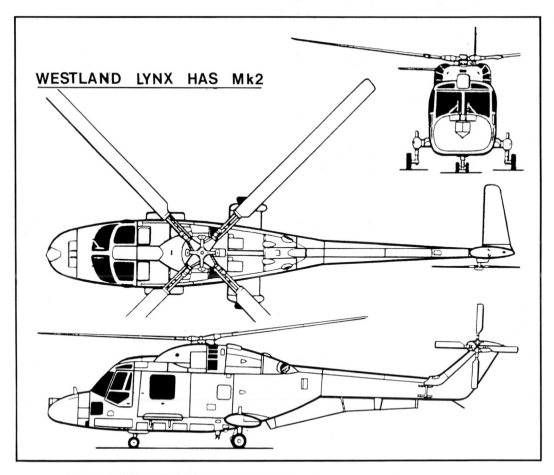

WESTLAND LYNX HAS Mk2

Above:
Westland Lynx HAS Mk 2.

Left:
Fixed to the flight deck by the harpoon engaged in the grid, the Lynx has nylon lashings attached for additional safety. Air engineers carry out checks to the two Gem engines. *MoD*

Above:
The low flight deck receives its fair share of spray, especially when the ship is under helm and altering course. Nonetheless, there have been no accidents, and Lynx have safely operated from these decks in extreme weather conditions. *MoD*

Above right:
The pilot's view of the ship as he makes his final approach in foggy conditions. The Flight Deck Officer is standing just to the right of the hangar, holding his arms up to wave the helicopter on to the deck. The recovery can be done without any radio transmissions. *MoD*

slow (maximum 104kt) and of limited endurance and weapon-carrying capacity. Thus the introduction of the Lynx was a considerable step up in the Type 21s capability.

The Lynx is a high-performance, all-weather helicopter, crewed by a pilot and an observer. It incorporates significant advances in rotor head, rotor blade and transmission technology to give improved reliability and reduced requirements for maintenance. It is twin-engined, with two Rolls-Royce Gem gas turbines of low specific fuel consumption which provide high margins of power for overwater operations in hot climates, or safe single-engine operation.

The RN Lynx HAS 2 grew from a design for an Army tactical helicopter in the mid-1960s. The first RN version flew in 1972, but it took a further five years of development before 702 Squadron was formed to train crews for operational work. Flight trials took place on board HMS *Amazon* in 1977. The first of the class to receive her own Lynx was HMS *Arrow* in 1978, and the last was HMS *Active* in 1986. Individual Type 21s have their own Flight, but all helicopters belong to the HQ 815 Squadron, based at Portland.

Operations from the flight deck took a major step forward with the introduction of the Lynx. A hydraulically-operated harpoon deck lock automatically secures the helicopter after touchdown to a steel grid on the ship's deck. It then can be rotated on its own axis around this harpoon for positioning prior to take-off or alignment with the hangar. Whilst the exact moment of landing has to be judged to give a reasonably steady deck, it can operate in high sea states. The tricycle undercarriage with two-stage oleos provides high energy absorption and stability on a rolling deck. Immediately after a landing negative pitch can be applied to hold the helicopter on deck by its downward thrust. Rough-weather flying operations are entirely feasible, but one of the drawbacks of the Type 21s design is the height of the flight deck above the waterline. At only 12ft high, it is not unusual to get a lot of spray and even the occasional wave across the deck. This tends to be unpopular with the Flight, and is none too good for the helicopter. The flight deck nets, which are lowered to the horizontal during flying operations, get buffeted and sometimes damaged in heavy seas.

The helicopter is stowed in the hangar, but has to have its main rotor blades and tail pylon folded to fit into the confined space. Hydraulic winches assist the flight deck team in moving the Lynx into the hangar.

Reconnaissance

The first role to describe is that of reconnaissance, for the Lynx is the eyes and ears of the Type 21. Capable of flying for four hours or so (with extra fuel tanks) at speeds of up to 150kt, it can cover many thousands of square miles. It can do this using its Ferranti Seaspray search and tracking radar, its built-in electronic support measures (ESM) receivers, and by the naked eye. Searches can thus be active or passive, depending upon the operational situation. A Decca *Tactical Air Navigational System* (TANS) gives the Observer his geographical position from which to report his contacts. This he can do either by using his High Frequency or Ultra High Frequency radio

(using codes to hide his meaning), or by waiting until he returns from the sortie to debrief the ship verbally.

Anti-Submarine

Helicopters originally embarked in frigates to provide a long-range anti-submarine weapon system, and whilst their roles have increased in number, the Anti-Submarine role remains of great importance. The Lynx can carry two torpedoes (Mk 46 or Stingray) or depth-charges, and will drop them on a submarine contact that is being reported to it by a ship,

helicopter, or even Nimrod Maritime Patrol Aircraft. The great advantage is that when its weapons have been expended, the helicopter can return to 'mother' (or another deck if more convenient) to rearm. The RN Lynx has no location device to find a submarine, though other navies equip theirs with sonar and sonar buoys. The equipment known as MAD — *M*agnetic *A*nomaly *D*etector — is due to be fitted to some RN Lynx: this detects small disturbances in the earth's magnetic field, such as might be caused by a submerged submarine.

Anti-Surface Vessel

Another potent role of the Lynx is against enemy surface vessels. Using its radar, it can detect small targets, even in the presence of strong sea clutter and electronic counter-measures. Armed with four Sea Skua ASV missiles, it can remain on task for 1½ hours and carry out an attack by day or night.

Sea Skua, built by British Aerospace, is an all-weather guided missile that is effective against targets ranging from missile-firing fast patrol boats to destroyers. It is a semi-active, radar-homing, sea-skimming missile, designed for high reliability, ease of maintenance and low life-cycle costs.

The Lynx has an additional important function when operating with the Type 21, when it acts as a reporting unit, identifying the enemy position and reporting this back to the frigate, so that it can fire its Exocet missiles at their maximum range. This process is known as Over The Horizon Targeting (OTHT).

Search and Rescue

A secondary, but important, role for the Lynx is Search And Rescue (SAR). Rapid reaction time, high speed, long range and an all-weather day and night capability are significant advantages of the RN Lynx in this role. A hydraulic winch can be mounted in the rear starboard door and this, operated by the Observer, can either lower an aircrewman down to rescue a person,

Above:
A Lynx drops an anti-submarine torpedo, which has its speed retarded by a parachute. Once in the water, the torpedo will commence its own search for the submarine. Two torpedoes can be carried by the Lynx. *MoD*

Below:
Armed with four Sea Skua anti-ship missiles, the Lynx makes a formidable foe. Its own search radar, sited in the nose, together with ESM receivers, make it most effective in the search and attack role. *MoD*

using a double harness, or can lower just a single harness to an uninjured man. The winch has a lifting capacity of 600lb and seating can be provided for up to 10 people. SAR operations are commonplace for the Type 21 frigates and their helicopters, with yachts in distress, crashed aircraft, and men from merchant ships either lost overboard or requiring medical assistance being relatively commonplace. Not surprisingly, these operations normally take place in extreme weather conditions that test the aircrew and flight-deck teams very severely.

Miscellaneous Tasks

In a casualty evacuation configuration, three field stretchers can be carried in the cabin, together with seating for two medical attendants.

Vertical replenishment and the transfer of stores between ships are further activities that are the day-to-day business of the aircraft.

Troop-carrying is possible with a six-man canvas seat being placed in the after cabin. The Falklands War saw Type 21s and their Lynx covertly inserting special forces into the islands by night. Further war experience confirmed the operational value of spotting the fall of shot from the ship's 4.5in guns on shore targets. The standard training given to the Observer to watch where the shot lands in relation to the target and then give 'corrections' back to the ship allows the frigate to lay down highly accurate fire from over the horizon.

Above:
Winching is frequently practised, and quite often put into serious use for SAR missions. The Flight Deck Officer, holding his hand aloft to show all is well, has communications with the helicopter, the Operations Room and the bridge. *MoD*

Below:
Whilst not big enough to take large helicopters, the flight deck does provide the space for vertical transfers of staff and stores. Additionally, large aircraft can embark fuel by hauling up a special fuel hose whilst they hover above. *MoD*

8 The Ship's Company

One of the radical requirements of the Type 21, as described in the first chapter, was for a much smaller complement than had been known in previous ships of this size. A reduction by approximately a third was achieved from frigates such as the 'Leander' class, which originally went to sea with about 260 onboard. When *Amazon* first sailed with a ship's company of 170, the Royal Navy had never seen such a diminutive crew for the size of ship, and the results were perhaps predictable: the workload for those onboard

increased considerably, and duties were sometimes taken on at a lower rate than had previously been the case. These seeming disadvantages were countered by increased delegation, improved job satisfaction, and much better living conditions.

The initial number in the complement has gradually crept up over the years, and is now just under 200. Inevitably, with the change of emphasis from shore training to sea training, there are a considerable number of additional training billets for officers, artificers and new entry ratings. Some departments were found to be seriously undermanned, with an unacceptable workload, and so numbers were increased — albeit by only one or two in order to make life tolerable. Nevertheless, the size of the ship's company remains unique in the Royal Navy, and only with the introduction of the Type 23 frigate, will the numbers be lessened still further.

Below:

For the family album. This photograph gives a good idea of the 200 or so members of the ship's company (though it must be remembered that the watchkeepers are still closed up below). With a crew of this size everyone knows each other, and this engenders a friendly spirit in the ship. *MoD*

Operations Department

First Lieutenant

MAA	CBM (PO)		NO
LREG	L/S (SEA)		CORRO
LPT			
LMA			

| PWO (A) | PWO (U) | SCO | Pilot & Observer |

Missile	Sonar	Comms.	Flight
		Tactical / *General*	
COP 1	PO 2	Yeoman 1 / Radio Supervisor 1	COP 2
PO 2	LS 2	LRO 1 / LRO 3	PO 2
LS 4	AB 4	RO 5 / ROI 3	LAEM 1
AB 3	S 4	RO 3	AEM 2
S 3			

EW	Radar
PO 1	CPO 1
LS 2	PO 1
AB 2	LS 8
S 2	AB 8

Below left:
The bridge team at work during Action Stations. The Navigating Officer takes a bearing, noted down by the midshipmen under training, whilst the Officer of the Watch peers through his binoculars. Beyond him is the helmsman at the ship's 'wheel'. *MoD*

Right:
Loading the expendable bathythermograph probe. This measures the temperature of the sea as it plummets downwards, showing the variations according to depth, and giving the ship figures from which to calculate sonar ranges. The rating, from the Sonar Branch, is wearing a life jacket for safety, since although the photograph shows calm conditions, the quarterdeck is often awash. *MoD*

Far right:
In these days of electronics, visual signalling remains of considerable importance. It cannot be detected (outside limited ranges) and it cannot be jammed. Radio operators are still trained in Morse code and the use of the signal projector. *MoD*

To understand how this number of men is employed it is necessary to know the breakdown of departments within the ship and to have some knowledge of the inevitable hierarchy.

The company is split into four departments: Operations, Weapons Engineering, Marine Engineering, and Supply and Secretariat. Each of these departments, headed by a Lieutenant-Commander or Lieutenant, then has its own formal chain of command and series of sub-departments, each responsible for an important facet of the ship's operations.

In command of a Type 21 will normally be a Commander, probably in his late 30s after some 20 to 25 years in the Royal Navy. This will almost certainly be his first and only 'drive' as a Commander. One of the class (which one varies over the years) will be commanded by a Captain, who will also be the Captain of the

Fourth Frigate Squadron (Captain F4). The Fourth Frigate Squadron consists of all the Type 21s, and in this way the interests and problems of the squadron are brought together by him and his small staff as part of the administrative chain of command. Captain F4 is often, but not invariably, someone who has had previous command of a Type 21.

Operations Department

The *Head Of Department* (HOD) is the First Lieutenant — also known as the *Executive Officer* (XO). He is very much the second in command of the ship, and deputises frequently for the Captain. Of middling seniority as a Lieutenant-Commander he will be a seaman, either a Warfare Officer or perhaps a sub-specialist such as an aviator or a submariner. On his shoulders falls the day-to-day running of the routine of the ship, its morale and efficiency, its appearance and cleanliness. Although of equal status to the other HODs, the First Lieutenant can be regarded as the SuperHOD, co-ordinating the activities of all departments to ensure a smooth-running ship.

The Operations Department consists of six sub-departments: Missile, Sonar, Radar, Electronic Warfare, Communications and Flight. Some 80 ratings from these divisions are trained to man and fight the sensors and weapons of the Type 21. They also maintain and clean the entire outside of the ship, and a proportion of the inside. It is no mean task to maintain the usual high standards of operability and appearance. The seamen make up the main part of the Operations Department, the exceptions being the Radio Operators in the Communications Division, and the Air Engineers of the Flight. As well as their operational skills, the seamen have the knowledge to carry out the tasks of taking away the boats, recovering men overboard, towing, handling berthing wires and replenishing at sea. Here it is worth noting that a replenishment at sea may have to be carried out whilst a ship is closed up to fight, and for this reason other non-seaman departments are trained up and used in this seamanship evolution.

Two ratings onboard are specifically trained in seamanship in order to provide deep

Left:
Replenishment at sea is very much a seamanship evolution, but is often carried out by members from the ME and WE Departments. This allows the Operations Department to remain closed up at the weapons in case of attack. Here the RAS team in *Ambuscade* is hauling in on the gun line to heave across the fuel hose. The spray in the foreground illustrates that they can expect to get wet.
MoD

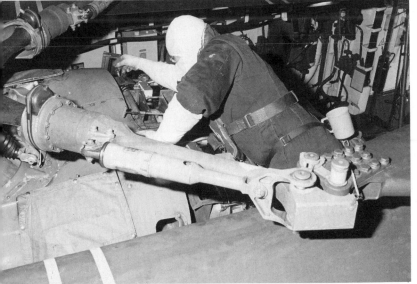

Left:
An Air Engineer from the flight works on one of the engines. The Lynx is stowed in the hangar with the blades folded. The ship is at action stations, and the rating is wearing anti-flash protective hood and gloves. The plastic mug slung on his life belt strap is there in case there is the opportunity for a 'whet' of tea or lime juice. *MoD*

Below left:
The Ship Control Centre, the heart of the mechanical world. A Chief of the Watch supervises his team from the chair, whilst a Petty Officer mans the power control levers on the left. These control the Olympus or Tyne gas turbines, depending which is engaged. The ME Department controls all the machinery from this compartment. *MoD*

Right:
Whilst the machinery spaces are unmanned, watchkeepers carry out routine rounds in them and undertake maintenance. Here a Marine Engineering Mechanic is seen on the deck plates. *MoD*

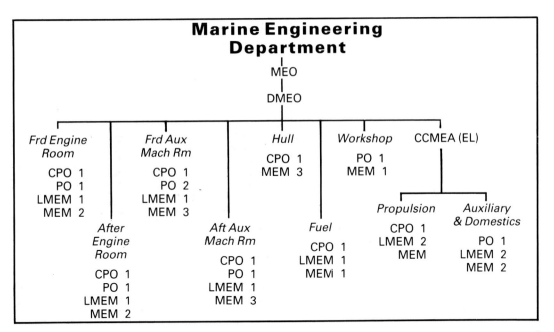

Marine Engineering Department

MEO

DMEO

Frd Engine Room	Frd Aux Mach Rm	Hull	Workshop	CCMEA (EL)
CPO 1	CPO 1	CPO 1	PO 1	
PO 1	PO 2	MEM 3	MEM 1	
LMEM 1	LMEM 1			
MEM 2	MEM 3			

After Engine Room	Aft Aux Mach Rm	Fuel	Propulsion	Auxiliary & Domestics
CPO 1	CPO 1	CPO 1	CPO 1	PO 1
PO 1	PO 1	LMEM 1	LMEM 2	LMEM 2
LMEM 1	LMEM 1	MEM 1	MEM	MEM 2
MEM 2	MEM 3			

expertise for the evolutions, and to maintain all the associated equipment and gear. The *Chief Bosun's Mate* (CBM), known by all as the Buffer, is a Petty Officer Seaman, and he is assisted by a Leading Hand.

Seamen Officers of the Operations Department make up the bulk of the members of the Wardroom. In addition to the XO will be two *Principal Warfare Officers* (PWOs), Lieutenant-Commanders or Lieutenants, the senior of the two being the Operations Officer. These officers are vital to the operation of the ship, being the men who direct the minute-by-minute running of the ship in its fighting mode. Below them come normally three Bridge Watchkeeping Officers, the senior of whom will be the Navigating Officer, responsible for the bridgemanship and safe navigation of the ship. The other two will have a plethora of more minor jobs which ensure the smooth running of the department. Finally, two Fleet Air Arm Lieutenants, a pilot and an observer, make up the team within the department. Every officer has important divisional duties in looking after the training, welfare and discipline of their men.

Marine Engineering Department

The Marine Engineering Department of the Type 21 consists of some 46 men. The Head of Department is the *Marine Engineer Officer* (MEO), who will be a Lieutenant-Commander or possibly a Lieutenant on the Special Duties list, one who has come up through the ranks and thus had broad experience. The Deputy MEO is a Warrant Officer Marine Engineer Artificer, and this in itself represents a breakthrough for the Type 21 in the scheme of complement. In the history of the modern frigate this class has replaced the traditional Lieutenant DMEO with the WOMEA, thus giving the latter a unique position of responsibility at sea. Qualified for the 'charge' duties, it can be argued that in this role the Warrant Officer is achieving his true place in the hierarchy of a ship. Certainly it is seen to be one of the most rewarding and satisfying jobs to be had by a senior rating.

The ME Department is split into sections based on ship design and equipment. The four

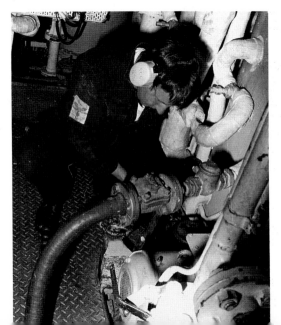

Weapons Engineering Department

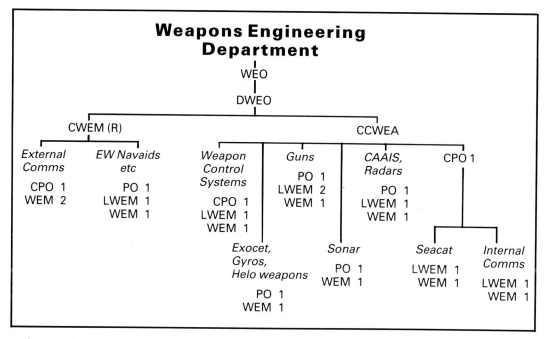

WEO
|
DWEO

CWEM (R)

- **External Comms**
  - CPO 1
  - WEM 2
- **EW Navaids etc**
  - PO 1
  - LWEM 1
  - WEM 1

CCWEA

- **Weapon Control Systems**
  - CPO 1
  - LWEM 1
  - WEM 1
  - **Exocet, Gyros, Helo weapons**
    - PO 1
    - WEM 1
- **Guns**
  - PO 1
  - LWEM 2
  - WEM 1
  - **Sonar**
    - PO 1
    - WEM 1
- **CAAIS, Radars**
  - PO 1
  - LWEM 1
  - WEM 1
  - **Seacat**
    - LWEM 1
    - WEM 1
- **CPO 1**
  - **Internal Comms**
    - LWEM 1
    - WEM 1

major machinery spaces each have a Chief Petty Officer Artificer in charge of a party of some five ratings responsible for the maintenance, repair and cleanliness of the space and the equipment within it. Given the constraints of space and the fact that much machinery is constantly running at sea, this task is a very considerable one. Today's 'stoker', as he is still called, though trained in technology unknown to his predecessor, remains caught up in duties such as wheeling spanners, scrubbing deckplates and carrying out safety rounds that might be recognised in the warships of the beginning of the century.

Outside the obvious machinery spaces come a mass of systems that stretch throughout the entire ship: electrical supplies, lighting, ventilation, firemain, fresh water and sundry domestics. Additionally there are the systems controlling the steering and propulsion of the ship. Responsibilities for these two lies mainly with the CPO Marine Engineering Mechanic and the CPO Marine Engineer Artificer (Hull), (known universally as the Chief Stoker and the Chippy respectively), and the CPOMEA(L), who looks after the electrical side. Each CPO again has a small party of subordinates working under him. There are 46 complement billets within the ME Department, with training billets for another four or so.

Weapons Engineering Department

The Weapons Engineering Department is not too dissimilar to its counterpart. A Lieutenant-Commander (or possibly Lieutenant) as HOD is assisted by a deputy who is now invariably a junior officer. When the Type 21 first went to sea, the DWEO was a Warrant Officer like the DMEO, but this changed in the late 1970s because of the difficulty in getting WE officers to sea early in their careers in order to broaden their experience.

The department is basically subdivided into Weapons and Radio Sections, and there are eight subsections each looking after a particular group of weapons, sensors, computers or communications. Each is headed by an artificer, who may be a Chief or Petty Officer — or even a Leading Rate — and under him will be one or two Leading Weapon Engineering Mechanics (LWEM) and one WEM. Overseeing all the sections are a Chief WEM, who co-ordinates the work of the department, and a Charge Chief, who manages the planned maintenance system.

Each subsection is responsible for keeping its electronic equipment up to peak performance. Regular checking and maintenance is required. The sensors, such as radar, sonar and electronic warfare receivers, are only 100% effective with this constant monitoring and fine adjustment. They work best when switched on and left transmitting, yet in modern tactics, where a warship will operate silently for most of the time so as not to give away its position, they are expected to work perfectly when switched on after, say, days of silence — a tall order indeed, and one

demanding great professionalism from the WE staff.

Perhaps surprisingly, there are only some 30 men in the WE Department, of them, 10 are likely to be senior ratings.

Supply and Secretariat Department

Smaller still, but as vital as any, is the Supply and Secretariat Department, which comes under a Lieutenant. Skills and responsibilities are wide-ranging, as this team has to provide support to every aspect of running the ship.

'An army marches on its stomach', and food is held dear to the ship's company: good food well presented is greatly appreciated, but the reverse can have a noticeable effect on morale. A Petty Officer Cook supervises a team of seven chefs working in the two galleys. He will work in conjunction with a Petty Officer Caterer to draw up a varied, healthy menu with three

or four choices for the main meals. The PO Caterer has a strict budget to keep to, and is responsible for ordering and storing the food. He has one assistant. Fresh provisions are used where possible, but frozen and dried foods play their part and have to be regularly rotated to keep them from going out of date. A ship may deploy for unexpected operations, and has to be stored accordingly.

A cafeteria system of feeding is used in Type 21s by both senior and junior ratings, but the Wardroom is served by stewards, who have an important role to play when the ship is giving official entertainment. Four stewards come under the direction of a Chief Petty Officer, who also acts as the Department Co-ordinator within the management structure of the ship.

Stores are as vital as food in the day-to-day running of a warship, and the Stores sub-

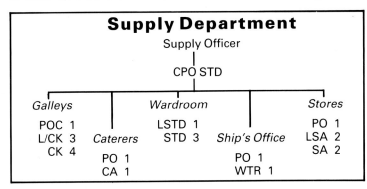

Supply Department

Supply Officer

CPO STD

Galleys		Caterers	Wardroom	Ship's Office	Stores
POC 1			LSTD 1		PO 1
L/CK 3		PO 1	STD 3	PO 1	LSA 2
CK 4		CA 1		WTR 1	SA 2

department is headed by a Petty Officer who is assisted by four stores accountants. They look after hundreds of thousands of items both large and small, valuable and consumable, varying from spare helicopter engines to tins of brass polish. Theirs is a never-ending business of ordering, storing, stocktaking and issuing. They provide a 24hr service every day of the year. Not surprisingly, a computer is used to assist them in their stocktaking task, and this computer is named OASIS. Specially designed software for onboard stores support has also been expanded to give catering and word-processing facilities as well. With only four terminals onboard at present, it is intended to expand the system vastly in the near future to provide many more terminals to be available to the ship's company. Personnel records will then be added.

Finally, there is the Ship's Office, manned by a Petty Officer Writer and a Writer. They have responsibility for handling the cash and correspondence. The Supply Officer himself is the custodian of the ship's accounts, and looks after the bulk of cash onboard, which may include a considerable amount of foreign currency according to the ship's programme. The PO Writer will hold some £5,000 in order to cash cheques for the ship's company. He also looks after the many allotments, allowances and claims. Everyone's pay is now handled by a shore establishment, HMS *Centurion*, and monthly payments are made by computer directly into the individual's bank account. The Writers are available to deal with pay enquiries.

The inevitable paperwork of the ship is shuffled by the Correspondence Officer, normally a young Sub-Lieutenant or Lieutenant whose primary duties are as a bridge watchkeeping officer. It is an ideal job in which to learn something of the administration of the Royal Navy. There is one exception to this 'Corro', in the Captain of the Squadron's ship. He has a Supply Officer in his first appointment acting as his secretary, as the 'Leader' has a far heavier workload of correspondence because he is the next step up the ladder of administration. A Writer works alongside the officer for logging in and out all the letters and returns, and for doing the typing. It is worth recording that all Type 21s also carry a Leading Writer who, rather strangely, is within the Engineering Departments in the Scheme of Complement. He runs the Technical Officers' correspondence, and works direct to the Engineering Officers.

The Miscellaneous Division

It is unfair to leave some of the key people of the ship's company until the final section but they do not fit into the other departments mentioned above.

The *Master At Arms* (MAA) has a very important position and function onboard, being the senior member of the lower deck. Responsible for disciplinary matters, he is a member of the Regulator Branch and has an

expert knowledge of the Naval Discipline Act. Perhaps a full-time job once upon a time, administering discipline normally takes up little time, and the Master's primary duty is as Whole Ship Co-ordinator, a key man ensuring the busy activities of each department do not clash, and planning ahead with the departmental co-ordinators, the Operations Officer and First Lieutenant. A number of other jobs can come the way of the Master, including that of Flight Deck Officer.

A Leading Regulator works alongside the Master, carrying out routine administrative duties such as monitoring the movements on and off the ship and acting as the postman.

Two further Leading Hands have very individual jobs onboard. The Leading Medical Assistant (LMA) mans the sick bay. He has sufficient knowledge to look after the day-to-day medical problems of the ship's company, and to take holding measures in emergency cases where a doctor's assistance is required. The Squadron has one Medical Officer, who moves around the ships and joins any that is deploying to an operational area. The second 'Killick' (the nickname given to a Leading Hand because of the killick anchor badge worn on his arm) is the Leading Physical Trainer (LPT), who has the responsibility of organising all the sporting and recreational activities, which range from expeditions to inter-mess quizzes. Other duties he normally takes on will include running the Communal Party, which is a small team made up by a rating from each department to clean the dining halls and man the scullery. Whilst the ship is operating in Defence Watches — that is, closed up for long periods of operations — the LPT and Leading Regulator will act as Quartermasters, alternating each watch on the ship's wheel. They also 'take the wheel' for special evolutions such as entering or leaving harbour or replenishing at sea.

Squadron Staff

The Captain of the Fourth Frigate Squadron has a small staff to help him administer the six ships. Two Commanders, a Marine and a Weapons Engineer (SMEO and SWEO) are the senior members. A Warfare Officer Lieutenant-Commander acts as the Squadron Operations Officer (SOO), and helps monitor the operational effectiveness of the Squadron. To look after the spiritual needs of the men there is the Squadron Chaplain (or Padre), and on the temporal side the Squadron Instructor Officer (SIO) assists the Education Officers in each ship to further the academic attainments of the ships' companies. Finally, a Squadron Medical Officer completes the team.

These staff officers, whilst based in the Leader's ship, have to move from frigate to frigate to carry out their duties. Not only do they add their expertise to any problem, they also can pass on the solutions previously worked out in other ships. Their close co-operation with the shore authorities is a key to the success of the Squadron.

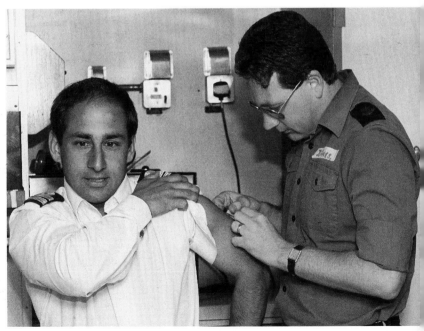

Far left:
A Leading Cook works his food processor. The wardroom galley, shown here, is small compared to the main galley, but contains essentially the same equipment. *MoD*

Left:
Keeping track of many thousands of small items of stores, this Leading Stores Accountant is in one of the several small storerooms that are sited through the ship. A computer assists him in his tasks. *MoD*

Right:
This won't hurt, Sir! The Leading Medical Assistant at work in his sick bay. He is normally the only medical cover to be had in a Type 21, but he is highly trained to cope with emergencies as well as carry out routine work such as this innoculation. *MoD*

9 The Twenty-One Club

It is to a sailor entirely natural to talk of 'the spirit of a ship', for every ship has its own individual spirit. To define it is like attempting to define the soul, for the steel hulk is devoid of it on build, and only acquires its spirit as the shipyard workers draw it together into the form of a ship whose company then moves onboard to set her to work. The officers, senior and junior ratings of the first commission create the spirit that will then motivate her through countless changes of personnel until the end of her working days. There are good ships and bad ships, happy and unhappy ships, and whilst the characters can change, it is surprising how ships retain their reputations

over the years. The Type 21 frigates have been most fortunate in being renowned for being most happy ships with a spirit that is peculiar to them alone.

A Captain who has commanded both a Type 21 and a Type 42 destroyer told the author that in the latter one had to work hard to achieve high morale, whereas in the former one had to

Below:
***Antelope** meets **Amazon** during her contractor's sea trials. She still wears the Red Ensign. From the very start the class were bonded by a unique spirit that has been with them ever since.*
Vosper Thornycroft

work still harder to destroy it. What brings about such a happy state of affairs?

First, there is pride in the ship itself. This is not special to the Type 21 alone, in that the first of any class will create much interest and certainly should be a source of considerable pride to the ship's company. The *Amazon* was revolutionary enough to exceed even the first-of-class norm: her unusual background caused extra notice to be taken of her. The fine appearance of the ship, coupled with the speed and acceleration to be had from the gas turbines gave a dash for which the class has been noted ever since. From the start the Type 21s have had a sports-car image, being handled with verve to show off their manoeuvring characteristics. Even to this day, when gas turbines are standard in new designs, they have kept the image. Being of lighter displacement than the Type 42s and Type 22s, they remain quicker off the mark and more manoeuvrable. Thus the dash remains. It is a personal opinion as to whether the looks have been surpassed by newer classes: perhaps it is telling that the Commanding Officer of a Type 21 which was visiting an overseas country in company with an aircraft carrier, a Type 42 and a Type 22 was asked what it was like to be in command of the newest ship in the force. He had to answer that his ship was older than the combined ages of the other three ships!

One feature that gave instant satisfaction was the standard of accommodation at every level. At long last it was felt that the designers had got it right; a great leap ahead had been achieved, and, as already stated, even today the standards are unsurpassed. An added benefit that was not readily apparent was in the layout of accommodation. Because it was centralised in one area of the ship for the entire ship's company, it gave rise to a feeling of community that is not easily achieved when messes are sited throughout the length of a ship. Communication through the different levels of the management seemed much easier and more natural — everyone felt they knew all that was going on, and no section of the company felt out on a limb.

Even the small size of the ship's company added to the spirit onboard. With fewer people to run the ship there was far more delegation, and men frequently undertook the work normally expected of the Rate above them. Inevitably they worked harder, but their job satisfaction compensated for that. What was most apparent was that every individual counted — there were no passengers, no room for anyone not to pull his weight to the full. A sense of achievement and fulfilment proved most rewarding, and again set these ships' companies apart from the rest of the Fleet.

From the dash that was inherent in the design came a style that was cultivated by each of the class as it commissioned. The ships' companies revelled in the image, and the spin-off was an enhanced spirit not just in the first ship but in the whole class. As the ships came into service, between 1974 and 1978, so emerged the Type 21 Club, the name informally given to the class group.

There was a natural bond between the ships: the pride and élan has already been described, but additionally there was a degree of scepticism, perhaps tinged with jealousy, in the rest of the Fleet. The 'not designed here' attitude still prevailed, and as a reaction there was a degree of defence in the ships clubbing together. Some would say that little has changed today.

A more practical benefit of the club stemmed from the requirement to look to each other to overcome problems unique to the ships. Very often the only expertise to be had in certain areas came from within the class. Consultation and co-operation flourished, and the bond between the ships grew ever stronger with social exchanges complementing the professional ones. Friendly rivalry was always present, and sporting fixtures took place whenever possible.

The Fourth Frigate Squadron

Until the 1980s the postwar Navy was divided into Flotillas, which were in turn divided into Squadrons consisting of a mixture of differing classes of frigates and destroyers. As the Type 21s commissioned, so they entered various squadrons: *Antelope* the Seventh, *Active* the Eighth, *Ambuscade* the Fifth, and so on. Of the eight Squadrons all but the First had one member of this class in it.

It then became broad policy to change the squadron make-up to a 'type' organisation in which ships of a similar class were to be members of the same Squadron. The Type 21s led the way when they joined together in the Fourth Frigate Squadron (4FS) in 1981 under the captaincy of Capt Hugo White. He had command of the Squadron of eight Type 21s, being the Captain of the Leader, HMS *Avenger*. His philosophy was to further in every way the fighting efficiency of the Squadron as the principal objective, but also to encourage the style and dash for which the ships were well known. His orders gave each commanding officer maximum freedom for individuality, and he constanty exhorted the ships to talk to each other at every level.

The 4FS was Devonport-based, and this added to the cohesion of the squadron and gave a very important stability to all the ships' companies. Guzz, as Devonport is affectionately known, is one of the Royal Navy's major bases, and countless naval families either originate from — or have moved to — the area. To know that a ship is permanently based near one's home has obvious attractions. There was a plan in late 1981 to split the

Squadron and base it in Portsmouth and Rosyth. The eight Type 21s were the largest Squadron and were not easy to administer by Captain 4FS, so a division would have eased such problems. Rosyth Dockyard previously had only steam ships, and there was the desire to send gas ships with advanced electronics to the base so that the work-force should keep up with the modern technology. The planned split and move was viewed with horror by the 4FS, being seen as a major threat to the cohesion of the Club, and on the personnel front an upset to home-port stability. Captain White and his staff opposed the plans forcefully, and succeeded in retaining the status quo. The 4FS remains today in Devonport, though now numbering only six frigates after the loss of *Ardent* and *Antelope* in the South Atlantic in 1982.

The 4FS also broke new ground in that her Captain had a technical staff that was unlatched from his ship. Previously, the Squadron Marine Engineer and Weapon Engineer Officers had been the Heads of Department in the Leader's ship. For the first time they were appointed in a separate capacity, able to move around the entire Squadron freely and as appropriate to the programmes of individual ships. Great benefits were achieved by this new organisation, which was subsequently copied by other squadrons.

The Type 21 Club has continued on the lines on which it started, and continues to thrive today. There is close co-operation at all levels, with professional and social contact much greater than that found in other squadrons. Newcomers to the Squadron frequently comment favourably on this fact. On the operational efficiency side there is keen competition for the Ferranti trophy, which is awarded by the Captain 4FS to the best all-round ship. On the sporting front there are frequent fixtures between the ships, and as often as possible, perhaps once or twice a year,

Left:
Avenger **sails from Portsmouth, a rare sight after the Type 21s became based at Devonport when they all joined the Fourth Frigate Squadron. In this photograph** ***Avenger*** **shows the number 2 on her funnel, indicating that she was then a member of the Second Frigate Squadron.**
MoD

Left:
Capt Hugo White stands proudly in front of a board showing the eight Type 21s that came under his command with the new formation of the Fourth Frigate Squadron.
MoD

Bottom:
A particularly rare sight, for warships operate for much of the time as single units. Here four ships (*Alacrity*, *Arrow*, *Amazon* and *Ardent*) steam in formation for a one-off squadron visit to Amsterdam in the autumn of 1981. *MoD*

there is a 4FS Olympiad — a sports afternoon involving many teams. Another regular feature is the Officers' Ball, where the Wardrooms combine in two ships alongside each other to bring their ladies onboard for a ball of a standard which would surprise the uninitiated.

Staying in the Club

One of the greatest strengths of the 21 Club is the way in which its members keep returning. It is not unusual to meet ratings who have spent six or more years in one ship (three years or less is the norm), having volunteered to stay on for longer. Even when drafted off for a spell of shoretime or a professional course, it is very common for men to volunteer to return to the Squadron. Indeed, the majority do so, and are welcomed back.

For the individual there are the advantages of going back to a class of ship that he likes. High on the list of reasons why he returns are the happiness of the class, the job satisfaction, and the accommodation. In particular, by volunteering for a Type 21 he knows that it will be Devonport-based. For the Navy it is advantageous to have people returning to ships in which they have had previous experience. If those people are keen to do so, so much the better! The constant return of members to the Type 21 Club is perhaps the greatest testament to the design of the ships and their mode of operation.

10 The Fighting Fourth in the Falklands War

The supreme test of any warship must be its ability to operate successfully in a hostile environment. Thankfully, it is rare that such a situation exists, and normally warships can be expected to fulfil their peacetime function of deterrence. Though the Royal Navy was involved in many minor confrontations in the years that succeeded World War 2, it had not seen major battle. The war in the South Atlantic in 1982 was to change that, and many classes of warship participated, from aircraft carrier to patrol vessel, nuclear submarine to minesweeper, together with numerous Fleet Auxiliaries and ships taken up from trade (known as STUFT). Britain's maritime power was quickly and effectively mobilised, and few in the Royal Navy were not involved in some way. The Type 21 frigates of the Fourth Frigate Squadron played a full and vital part in the conflict, with seven out of the eight in the class being involved. It is perhaps invidious to select the activities of one group of ships that provided only a part of the whole, but this chapter seeks to tell the story of the Twenty-One Club in the Falklands War to illustrate their wide-ranging capabilities as frigates, and the fighting spirit of the Squadron.

Preparation and Deployment

The Argentinian invasion of the Falkland Islands on 2 April 1982 found the Squadron, along with the rest of the Navy, about its normal business across the globe. *Amazon* was conducting the Armilla Patrol in the Gulf. She had relieved *Active,* who was on her way home via a large annual exercise off Gibraltar. *Arrow* was also involved in this exercise, and was the first Type 21 to head south. Meanwhile, *Alacrity* was engaged in syllabus training at Portland, and was prepared for war in 12 frenetic hours. Back in the Squadron's base port, Devonport, there was the Leader, *Avenger,* sitting in the bottom of a dry dock undergoing maintenance, together with *Antelope, Ardent* and *Ambuscade.*

Intense activity was seen in the preparation of the ships for war. On 5 April *Alacrity* and *Antelope* sailed from Devonport to meet up with a Royal Fleet Auxiliary (RFA) and four

Below:
Ardent heading south. This photograph, taken from SS Canberra, is after Ardent had laid on a firepower display for the troops soon after leaving Ascension Island. *MoD*

landing ships to escort them south, whilst four days later *Ambuscade* sailed, shrouded in secrecy and laden with ammunition for the Gibraltar garrison, to act as the Gibraltar guardship. *Arrow* was one of the initial elements of the Task Group to arrive at Ascension Island on 11 April, to be followed five days later by *Alacrity,* then *Antelope* and *Ardent.*

Material preparations on board were extensive. Luxuries were landed, be they personal articles or superflous fittings or furniture. Pictures, curtains and covers were removed, mirrors and formica sheets taken down or taped so that they might not become lethal projectiles after an explosion. Distinguishing marks such as funnel markings and pennant numbers were painted out, as were black waterlines, white bollards and any other signs of the 'tiddly' Navy. Cherished ships' boats, resplendent in blues and reds, became grey overnight. The ships did all they could to reduce their appearance as a potential target, especially to submarines and aircraft. On the offensive side, the helicopter-launched missile Sea Skua was added to the ships' arsenals well ahead of its clearance for use in the Fleet. *Ardent* even took some Stingray torpedoes south with her, having to work out tactics for their use. Training of personnel was intensi-fied, with emphasis on warfare and damage control. First aid teams were seen doubling around the ships carrying laden stretchers up and down ladders to get fit and into practice. Action working dress became the standard rig and antiflash hoods and gloves were worn continuously, whilst life jackets and respirators were carried by all on board wherever they went.

The task group's elements continued south from Ascension with the destroyers and frigates as close escorts. *Alacrity* suffered defects on the primary gearbox of her starboard Tyne, but after spares were air-dropped and some five days spent stoning the teeth of cogs, repairs were successfully completed (the gearbox continues to run today as repaired then!) and she caught up with the group.

First Action

Alacrity was the first ship of the Task Force to have contact with the enemy when she was directed to clear the Argentinian 'spyship' *Narwhal* from the Task Group as the force neared the Falklands. After chasing to within two cables, totally darkened, *Alacrity* directed the Argentinians to clear to the north, with the help of some acrimonious VHF exchanges and some starshell.

Alacrity and *Arrow* then detached with *Glamorgan* ahead of the *Carrier Battle Group* (CBG) towards the Falklands on 1 May to carry out the first of many bombardments of shore

targets. Port Stanley airfield was their target, but they came under attack from three Dagger aircraft which had approached unnoticed at high speed and at very low level. Opening fire with only close-range weapons, the ships were subjected to attack from cannon fire and 1,000lb bombs. *Alacrity* suffered some shock damage from a near miss, and *Arrow's* Seacat aimer was wounded, the ship sustaining superficial damage from cannonshell.

Alacrity's Lynx helicopter, airborne for spotting the fall of shot from the bombardment in the lee of Kidney Island, sighted a Coastguard patrol and attacked it with its door-mounted machine gun. Outgunned by the boat's 0.5in machine guns, the helicopter was beaten off, suffering several hits including partial severance of the main transmission drive shaft. This first day's action ensured the

21 Club was at the forefront of the initial action – in bombardment, in an attack on an Argentinian vessel, and under air attack.

On 2 May the two 21s were stationed in an anti-submarine screen around the CBG some 80 miles north-east of Port Stanley. The group was threatened by attack from the air, from submarines and from the Argentinian surface fleet, which was known to be at sea in force. Expectations of an attack were high, but after the risk of a dusk strike had passed, *Alacrity* and *Arrow* were detached for a further bombardment of Port Stanley airfield. The war at sea escalated fast with the sinking of the *Belgrano* on the 3rd and the *Sheffield* on the following day. In helping the stricken *Sheffield*, *Arrow* first passed hoses across for fire-fighting, and then later went alongside her to take off 225 survivors.

Reinforcements continued their way southwards. *Antelope* escorted her group to hand them over to *Antrim* before returning to Ascension as escort for RFA *Tidespring,* and with the special prisoner Lt Astiz (captured in South Georgia) and 15 members of the British Antarctic survey team onboard. *Ardent,* in company with *Argonaut,* was racing south, and *Ambuscade* was designated guardship for Ascension Island. A few days later *Avenger,* quickly refloated out of her dock, together with *Active* joined the *Bristol* group in UK waters, fully prepared for war.

Alacrity's Dash through the Sound

On 8 May *Alacrity* carried out an accurate bombardment of the Port Stanley area with spotting from her Lynx, and the following day she and *Arrow* took up patrols off the Falkland Sound, to the south and north respectively. Two days later *Alacrity* was ordered to transit the Sound, a difficult and dangerous mission in the narrow channels between rocks and reefs on a dark night, in low visibility and with the possibility of mines. As they neared the halfway point, a darkened ship was detected off Swan Island. When the ship took violent evasive action it was engaged with the 4.5in gun. The deck cargo – aviation fuel or explosives – caught fire and she blew up, sinking within 15min of her detection. It was the 834-ton transport *Isla de los Estados,* en route to Port Howard and Pebble Island. *Alacrity* continued north out of the Sound without detection, and rendezvoused with *Arrow* before turning eastward at very high speed to reach the cover of the Carrier Battle Group before dawn. Both ships were carrying out evasive steering and had torpedo decoys deployed, which proved fortuitous as they entered the patrol area of the submarine *San Luis,* which was tracking them and happened to be in an ideal position to attack. Her fire control computer was unserviceable and she was able to fire only one torpedo at a time, and then had to guide it manually. She fired at 500yd, but it is understood the control wire broke, and she was unable to carry out a further attack. It may be that the torpedo struck *Alacrity*'s 182 torpedo decoy, which was found to be badly damaged when next recovered.

A few days later, on the 15th, *Alacrity* repeated her transit with an uneventful passage. She landed two Gemini boat-loads of Special Boat Service Marines into Grantham Sound, having used her Lynx as a diversion by

Below:
Falklands Islands.

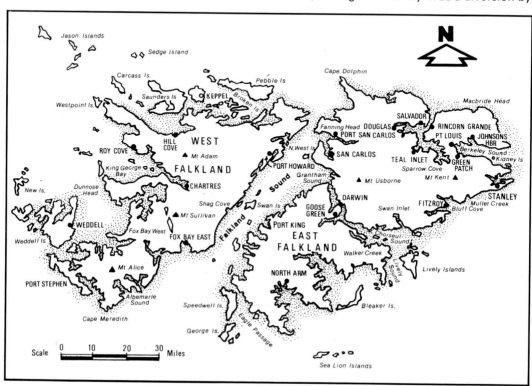

dropping flares on the Argentinians in Port Howard. This group carried out the vital final recce of the San Carlos area just to the north. *Alacrity* was forced to exit the Sound in bright moonlight less than three miles from the observation post of Fanning Head, amazingly without being sighted.

Escorting duties continued with *Alacrity* and *Arrow* amongst the screen of the CBG, and *Ardent* with the approaching amphibious group. *Ambuscade* and *Antelope* were proceeding south from Ascension Island, the former with one defective Tyne, which required her to use a Tyne/Olympus combination with its much higher fuel usage. In very high seas the two ships met with the tanker *British Esk,* which had the *Sheffield* survivors onboard. *Antelope* attempted to refuel by the astern method, but was unable to do so and continued south. *Ambuscade* had only some 10% of fuel left onboard, a critical level which required her to ballast two tanks with sea water to maintain minimum stability. She persevered with refuelling, and managed to replenish to some 80%. For the remainder of her passage south, Marine Engineer Mechanics were required to scrub out manually the fuel tanks that had been contaminated by the salt water — a particularly unpleasant job made worse by the rough seas.

Invasion, and loss of HMS *Ardent*

On 20 May the amphibious group, with seven escorts including *Ardent,* detached to take up stations for the re-invasion. *Ardent* led into the Falkland Sound at 30kt, surprisingly unseen, and took up station for bombardment in support of a diversionary air raid on Darwin. Early the next morning the SAS called for fire on Goose Green airfield, where the Pucaras were preparing for take-off. At a range of 22,000yd and close to the kelp beds, *Ardent* opened fire, and over the next few hours fired over 150 rounds of *H*igh *E*xplosive (HE), destroying at least one Pucara as it taxied for take-off. She could not, however, prevent Pucara operations, and herself drove off two of their attacks and a further attack by Daggers. Two Pucaras were repulsed by gun and Seacat, but an hour later a Skyhawk approached low overland and managed to straddle her with bombs. Surviving this attack, she continued her *N*aval *G*unfire *S*upport (NGS) for another hour before completing her fire mission, when she was ordered into the centre of Grantham Sound to deflect air-raids closing the amphibious group from the south. Three Argentinian navy A-4Qs were seen manoeuvring to attack the ship, which was turned into wind at maximum possible speed on two Tynes in order to complicate the aircrafts' fire control problem. As the A4s closed, the helm was put over, but the gun could not be brought to bear and the Seacat, which had fired three missiles already that day, refused to fire. The close-range weapons failed to impede the attack, and three of the nine 500lb bombs which were aimed at her found their target, two exploding in the hangar, and the third, which did not explode, ending up in the after Auxiliary Machine Room. Some 10 officers and ratings were killed instantly, including Lt-Cdr Sephton who was last seen firing a sub-machine gun into the underside of an attacking aircraft. The Lynx was destroyed and the Seacat launcher blown 80ft into the air, falling back on to the flight deck. Damage was severe, with fires in the hangar, and flooding in the dining hall and Ship Control Centre from fractured firemain pipes. The 4.5in gun was out of action through loss of power, and with the Seacat gone completely there were only close-range weapons for defence. However, the engines remained running, giving 17½kt, and *Ardent* was told to close the San Carlos anchorage as the damage control parties tackled the fire and flood. Minutes later three Dagger aircraft attacked with bombs, but achieved only straddles.

Twenty minutes or so elapsed before a fresh raid of three Skyhawks attacked from the port quarter with 500lb retard bombs, scoring at least two more hits aft, and killing or wounding all the after damage control parties who were engaged in fighting the previous fires. Yet another attack by three Mirage aircraft added to the confusion, but caused no further damage. The engines were still running, but the steering gear was out of action, and the ship was heavily ablaze aft and rushing at 18kt towards an island at the north-eastern corner of Grantham Sound. Somehow the engines were stopped and an anchor released, halting the ship some 800yd from the rocks.

From what could be made out from beyond the smoke and flames, the ship was holed aft and much water was being taken on (probably, as it turned out, from a fractured firemain). It appeared that the after end of the ship had been blown away. There was imminent danger that the torpedo magazine would explode, and there were indications that the ship might quickly plunge stern first. In view of this and the lack of firefighting ability, the Captain decided to abandon ship before further raids developed. HMS *Yarmouth* was called alongside to take off the survivors. There were 37 wounded and 142 unhurt; 22 men died. The

Captain was the last to leave, some 50min after the attack, the fires still raging.

Ardent continued to burn, with occasional explosions, until she sank at 0200 the following morning. Only the top of her mast remained showing above the water, acting as a navigational warning of the wreck below, and as a datum which Arrow used when bombarding Goose Green later in the campaign. Of the six Argentinian navy A4s which attacked Ardent, only one returned unharmed to the Argentine. Interestingly, the Argentine navy proved better weaponeers than their air force counterparts, in that their bombs were fused correctly. However, this was the last strike action of the Navy A4s during the campaign. For Ardent, two Distinguished Service Crosses, a George Medal and four Mentions in Despatches were awarded as a result of the action.

Above:
The fire raging out of control, *Ardent* abandons ship. *Yarmouth* is alongside receiving the survivors dressed in their waterproof 'once-only' suits. Amazingly, some survivors escaped by fighting their way out of the bomb holes right aft and jumping into the water. *MoD*

To the east of the Falklands the carriers, carrying out intensive flying operations to support the assault with the RFAs and STUFT in company, were being screened by the remaining escorts, including Arrow and Alacrity. That day Antelope and Ambuscade joined the screen as the force zig-zagged to counter any enemy submarines in the area, all ships in a high state of readiness against possible attack, especially from the air. Ambuscade went in to replenish fuel, bumping the

Right:
A close-up of the extensive damage caused by the multiple bomb hits received aft by *Ardent*. **The hangar roof is ripped back and the Seacat launcher blown off. One rating, whose action station was on the Pedestal Sight in the exposed position just under the 912 radar tracker dish, was blown into the boat to be seen on the left of the picture. He was not seriously injured. Another, manning a machine gun in a similar position, was knocked unconscious as the deck lifted and hit him, but survived.**
MoD

tanker in the difficult station-keeping conditions. That night, whilst screening the major ships, *Ambuscade* gained firm sonar contact and heard the noise of a torpedo pass close by. Although it is believed that whales initiated a number of such encounters, the men holding the contact were convinced that this was not the case here, and it certainly appeared to be heading determinedly for the main body.

The Final Hours of HMS *Antelope*

Antelope entered San Carlos water before dawn on the 23 May, escorting the first

Below:
With the survivors off, *Ardent* **is left at anchor, having been hit by at least five bombs. The gun is frozen pointing to the sky, and the 992 radar aerial is toppled over to starboard. After several explosions she sank the following morning.** *MoD*

resupply convoy. Her Lynx attacked and hit a cargo vessel in Port King, which was found to be sinking on a later reconnaissance flight. On the return flight, the helicopter was attacked as four Skyhawks overflew it. Undamaged, the helicopter broadcast a warning to alert the frigates. The aircraft were engaged by a barrage of fire, but one pressed home to score a direct hit on the starboard side of *Antelope* below the hangar. The 1,000lb bomb failed to explode, and the aircraft, damaged by 20mm fire, hit the mainmast and exploded, falling into the sea just beyond the frigate. Another attack followed immediately from the port quarter, and a bomb was taken onboard below the bridge. Again, this failed to explode: the bombs were being released too near the target and the fuses were not arming.

With one bomb in her air conditioning unit and one in the badly damaged Petty Officers'

Above:
Antelope **enters San Carlos anchorage at action stations after her engagement. Two bombs are lodged unexploded on board, the hole caused by one being visible, in the ship's side under the foremast. Her mainmast is bent right over to port by the impact of a Skyhawk.** *MoD*

Mess, *Antelope* had lost her gyros and was lit between decks by emergency lighting. One man had been killed, and another seriously injured. The air attacks continued, and the frigate remained in her sector until they ceased, when she headed into San Carlos water and anchored close to HMS *Fearless* off Ajax Bay. Two Royal Engineer bomb disposal experts came onboard to tackle the bombs. Assisted by the ship's Mechanical Engineering Officer and a Mechanician, the team set about their work whilst the ship's company, bar those manning communications and the weapons, were moved to the upper deck. The bomb in the air conditioning unit proved difficult and a small defusing charge was used. As the four men returned to examine the results, the 1,000 pounder exploded, killing one RE and maiming the other. Amazingly, the other two were only slightly injured. Firefighting teams attacked the resultant fires, but the firemain had been damaged and soon the ship was ablaze on three decks across its width. The proximity of magazines made it imperative to abandon ship, an operation which was carried out by landing craft from *Fearless.* Ten minutes later the Seacat ready use magazine exploded, and then the main Seacat and torpedo magazines blew up. The fires continued through the night, and soon after dawn another massive explosion broke *Antelope*'s back and she sank midships, with her bow and stern pointing defiantly skywards.

Exocet Attack

For the next couple of days the intensity of the air attacks was maintained, whilst the amphibious operations continued largely unhindered. The escorts, *Arrow* amongst them, and the aircraft from the carriers took the pressure, whilst the CBG and STUFT supported the operations with *Alacrity* and *Ambuscade* amongst their escorts. The latter escorted ships out of San Carlos on 24 May, but it was the following day that, whilst screening the carriers, she detected the Agave radar of Argentinian Super Etendards – the Exocet missile carriers. Two of these aircraft had approached the force from the north-west. Climbing when 40 miles from *Hermes*, they transmitted their radars to search for a target. The alarm was raised, the aircraft were tracked on radar, and two Exocet missiles were seen to be launched some 22 miles from *Ambuscade*, the aircraft turning away and escaping. All the standard reactions were taken, with the gun and 3in chaff being fired and the ship manoeuvring to present the smallest possible target. The Exocets, now also being tracked visually by *Ambuscade,* closed on her on a steady bearing but then appeared to be seduced by her chaff. They flew through the chaff, and then at least one went on to hit the *Atlantic Conveyor,* a large container ship laden with vital stores and aircraft. Extensive damage was caused, and it was not long before the crew had to abandon ship. *Alacrity* and *Ambuscade* assisted and searched close to the ship for survivors. *Alacrity* came close alongside and made one attempt to lay on to

Above:
The 1,000lb bomb near to the Seacat magazine exploded whilst being defused, and caused massive fires. *Antelope* **is seen here with her back broken, and still on fire after a number of further explosions.** *MoD*

Right:
The end of a proud ship. *MoD*

the *Atlantic Conveyor,* but was forced to hold clear as munitions were by then exploding in the white-hot holds aft. A clutch of life-rafts were towed clear of the stricken ship, and 74 exhausted sailors and three bodies were taken up by *Alacrity.*

Naval Gunfire Support

The pattern of the war was starting to alter. The landing of troops had been achieved most successfully despite concentrated opposition from Argentinian aircraft. The escorts had taken the brunt of the attacks, and the cover provided by the Sea Harriers together with the valiant defence by the escorts over a number of days defeated the air offensive. The loss of the two 21s and then of HMS *Coventry,* together with a number of other ships damaged, was a heavy but strategically acceptable price to pay.

The CBG had to remain fully alert and ready to repulse attacks from above and below the surface. Air cover and strikes continued to further the battle ashore. The destroyers and frigates found themselves falling into a more routine life: escorting the CBG and STUFT, taking RFAs and merchantmen in and out of the Amphibious Operating Area (AOA), and carrying out shore bombardments. The inshore activities almost invariably took place under cover of darkness.

26 May saw *Arrow* escorting ships out of the AOA to hand them over to *Ambuscade* to take out to the carrier group. This was the day that the *Bristol* group, with *Avenger* and *Active* amongst it, arrived to boost greatly the RN force. Whilst *Ambuscade* and *Active* went about more escorting in and out of San Carlos, the next day *Avenger* and *Alacrity* set off with *Glamorgan* to bombard Port Stanley, firing 209 rounds of ammunition. *Arrow,* meanwhile,

was off Darwin supporting the 2 Para's attack with 135 rounds of HE and 22 starshell. It was during this evening that *Avenger* was overflown by a large missile, fired from ashore, which passed over her flight deck at a height of 5ft, giving at least her flight deck team a surprise. It now seems certain that this was the first firing of shore-based Exocet, happily fired with the incorrect weapon settings, which caused the missile narrowly to miss its target.

Whilst *Glamorgan* and *Ambuscade* put 190 rounds into the Port Stanley area on 29 May, *Avenger* was attempting to land Special Forces in East Falkland. Thwarted by bad weather, she resorted to shelling targets. *Arrow* went down the Falkland Sound to put 100 rounds into Fox Bay. These Naval Gunfire Support engagements were, as so often happened, opposed with inaccurate fire with 105mm guns from ashore. The next day, back with the CBG, another air attack took place — two Super Etendards with the last remaining air-launched Exocet, and four Skyhawks. Warned by *Ambuscade, Avenger* and *Exeter* detected the aircraft radars, and a heated AA action took place with Seadart and gun. *Avenger* claimed to shoot down the Exocet which was heading for her. Although this claim was subsequently disallowed, she did decoy one Exocet with chaff, and was the target for a number of bombs which were near misses. Between them *Exeter* and *Avenger* destroyed two Skyhawks in the action. That night *Avenger* successfully inserted Special Forces into the islands using

Ambuscade's Lynx, and then went on to shell enemy observation posts.

So the operations continued. Shelling by night (100 rounds was the norm, because of the impending shortage of 4.5mm Mk 8 ammunition, though *Avenger* fired a staggering 293 rounds on the night of 1 June), and returning to the CBG at dawn to replenish fuel and ammunition. The latter was done either alongside an ammunition ship ('FORT' class RFA) with jackstays rigged both forward and aft; or by helicopter underslung loads. The evolution could take hours and was exhausting work for the whole ship's company, which was required to hump the heavy ammunition, shell by shell, through the ship to the magazine entrance. Frequently the replenishments would be broken off as the force went to action stations in anticipation of an air strike. The weather was variable. Storms generated awesome seas, whilst on other occasions there was flat calm and thick fog. Either way, the operations continued unabated.

Arrow had been increasingly suffering from cracks in her superstructure, caused by the rough seas, and by the time spent grinding alongside *Sheffield* during her rescue

Below:
The 4.5in gun in action. The accuracy and reliability of the gun were much praised by the Army, who benefited ashore from the support. The seas are calm, being close inshore, but there is a strong wind whipping up the spume. *MoD*

Above:
Vital supplies and weapons were airdropped by the RAF into the war zone. Here a Type 21 (believed to be *Ambuscade*) manoeuvres to recover the stores. Regrettably, several of the containers sank. *Author's collection*

Below:
Avenger seeking to assist *Plymouth* after air attacks had left her damaged and on fire. *MoD*

attempts. On 31 May she went out to a safe haven further east of the Islands, where she had beams fitted on her upper deck to restore her longitudinal strength. Later, after the fighting had ceased, *Ambuscade* was to receive the same treatment.

On 3 June, divers reclaimed a 20mm gun and mounting from the wreck of *Antelope,* and this was immediately fitted in *Avenger* to augment her armament. Painted across the gunshield were the words 'Antelope's Avenger'. Night after night the Fourth Frigate Squadron continued to bombard the enemy ashore in support of the ground advance.

On 7 June *Alacrity* left the Falklands to return home, the first ship to do so. Her 4.5in gun had exceeded its life: 'Propose to go on until it drops off' had been the Captain's signal, but this was not allowed. Six days later, *Arrow* also detached. She had fired 902 rounds and was suffering from structural damage that required substantial repair.

That night four frigates entered Berkeley Sound, inside an Argentinian minefield, to assist in a barrage from shore artillery and mortars which was to precede an infantry attack. *Ambuscade* (firing 228 rounds) and *Yarmouth* supported 2 Para, whilst *Avenger* (156 rounds, taking her total to over 1,000) and *Active* supported the Scots Guards. On her way into the Sound that night, *Avenger* lost a propeller blade through metal fatigue: her speed was consequently reduced to 16kt on one shaft.

Above:
The fighting over, there was time to relax. Here the *Ardent* survivors line up on the deck of the *Queen Elizabeth 2* during their passage home. Their spirit is self-evident.
MoD

Right:
Snowballs on the Equator. Twenty snowballs were made of Falkland Islands' snow and kept in *Ambuscade's* deep freeze. They were auctioned for the South Atlantic Fund, and when the ship reached the Equator it stopped whilst the snowballs were thrown from the Southern to the Northern hemisphere.
Author's collection

Mopping-up Operations

That assault was to be the last. White flags were to be seen the following day, and the Argentinians surrendered. Whilst Gen Moore flew to Port Stanley to accept surrender, *Avenger* proceeded to Fox Bay, where 900 Argentinians surrendered to the ship. *Avenger's* ship's company then set about the cleaning-up operations, processing prisoners of war and giving the scattered settlements some technical support. The CBG remained vigilant at sea, with her screen of escorts still in place. After the exhilaration of victory it was important to keep guards up (hostilities had not officially ceased), but it was not easy to keep morale at a high peak when the daily routine lacked its previous injections of adrenalin and thoughts were turning increasingly to home.

Whilst *Avenger* was having a new propeller blade fitted in San Carlos Water, she and others erected a memorial to *Ardent* and *Antelope,* on a hill overlooking their watery graves. A bugler from *Active* sounded the Last Post, and a guard from *Avenger* fired a rifle salute. This memorial remains proudly standing, and is given the honour of being piped by warships passing it.

Ambuscade sailed in early July crammed full of a detachment of the 2nd Battalion Scots Guards. She took them to South Georgia to relieve M Company Royal Marines, who had retaken the island at the beginning of the war.

Above:
The Red Arrows salute *Arrow* as she enters Plymouth after the passage back from the South Atlantic. The pennant numbers, painted out on the way south, are starting to show again. *MoD*

Left:
First line across as *Ambuscade* comes alongside in front of her welcoming families. The reception for all ships returning was memorably overwhelming. *MoD*

She then took these on to Ascension Island. The other ships were detached in small groups, the last Type 21 to leave being *Avenger* at the end of August.

So ended a short but bitter conflict that gripped the attention of the world. The Type 21s had played a full role, being particularly to the fore as escorts and in shore bombardments. The loss of two of the class inevitably caused criticisms to be raised against their design and capabilities. Undoubtedly the aluminium superstructure made them more vulnerable to damage once on fire, but any modern warship coming under such heavy attack would be pushed to survive such punishing explosions. That the escorts were successful in supporting the assault and drawing off the attackers was all-important to the success of the whole operation.

Capt White, the Captain of *Avenger* and the Fourth Frigate Squadron, sent a ceremonial Argentinian sword handed to his first Lieutenant at Fox Bay to Rear-Adm Woodward. In his letter of thanks the Admiral wrote: 'My gratitude to the Fighting Fourth in this vicious six weeks is boundless, and their press-on spirit has not gone unnoticed. I am sad only at the cost in men and ships, and am proud of you all.' Adm Woodward returned the sword to Capt White.

Postscript: *Amazon,* much frustrated to be the only Type 21 not to be involved in the fighting, arrived off the Islands in August 1982 to take up patrol.

Summary of Bombardment
25 April-14 June 1982

Avenger	1,075	*Yarmouth*	1,441
Arrow	902	*Glamorgan*	1,245
Active	633	*Plymouth*	490
Alacrity	587	*Cardiff*	288
Ambuscade	460	*Glasgow*	288
Ardent	163	*Antrim*	286
		Exeter	44
		Coventry	14

Right and below:
The Type 21 memorial stands overlooking the now calm waters of San Carlos. It serves as a permanent reminder of those who died during the conflict. Warships salute their memory by piping the still as they pass the memorial. *MoD*

11 The Future

There is no set length of time to a warship's life, for much depends on how the ship has fared over the years with her operational role in the prevalent weather; the pattern of her refitting; the effectiveness of her modernisations; the state of her equipment and machinery, and the condition of her hull as regards strength. A further factor is the operational requirement for the ship: would it be cost-effective to continue running it, and would it be needed to maintain Fleet strength? Sixteen years of service was once quoted for the 'Leander' class frigate, yet the oldest of this class still serving was first commissioned some 24 years ago. Two of the 'Rothesay' Improved Type 21 frigates decommissioned in 1988 after an honourable 30 years of service. What can be expected of the Type 21? Twenty years or so is the figure currently being worked upon, indicating that the oldest of the class, HMS *Amazon*, can be expected to decommission in the early to mid-1990s, but this may be reviewed as previous classes have been. It may also be borne in mind that these will be the first gas ships to go, and therefore the state of the machinery could well be assessed as being significantly different from the ageing steam ships.

Improvements to Date

A striking feature of the class is how little their configuration of weapons and sensors has changed since the design stage. The Type 21 was designed as an interim frigate with no margins for later modernisation of its weapon fit, and therefore there has been no major mid-life update for the class as compared with the Batch II and III 'Leanders'. Those Type 21s not built with the Exocet missile or Ship Torpedo Weapon System (STWS) were retrofitted in later refits (with the exception of *Amazon*, which never got STWS). The Lynx helicopter joined the class when it became operational (1977 onwards), and was armed with the Sea Skua missile from 1982. Two extra Oerlikon guns were fitted aft after the Falklands conflict, but otherwise the firepower of the class has remained the same. The CAAIS computer has had updated software to improve its performance, but this is a constant and relatively simple process.

A small number of features have altered the ships' appearance over the years. The small waist either side of the hangar has been partially covered in with *Amazon*, *Active* and *Alacrity*, and the mainmast in all ships has been streamlined and now carries two VHF radio aerials wrapped around the upper pole mast. Two sensors which were retrofitted and altered the appearance were the navigational radar Type 1006, which replaced the Type 978, and the ESM aerials which were placed on the foremast under the Type 992 radar platform.

Perhaps the most noticeable improvement has been the hull strengthening that took place in the mid-1980s during refits. Fatigue cracks in

Left:
Active showing the class with its mid-1980s weapon fit. The SCOT satellite communication aerials are not fitted, but these can be added on when operations dictate the need.
MoD

95

the aluminium superstructure of the Type 21s had occurred frequently, one reason being that aluminium is more susceptible to fatigue cracking than steel. These cracks were troublesome rather than dangerous, and were repaired by welding. However, measurements taken of stresses to the steel hulls of the class showed that strengthening was required. The South Atlantic war took a heavy toll on the class with severe conditions, high speeds in very rough seas, and operations alongside other ships during rescue attempts. Emergency strengthening was applied to some of the class whilst in the South Atlantic in the form of girders not dissimilar to railway lines being bolted on to 01 deck midships. For long-term hull strengthening all ships later received stiffening by having a thicker plate bolted on to the external ship's side, some 100ft long and 2ft high, just below the level of Number One deck. This addition, readily apparent to the eye, has been extremely successful, and it is said that the class now has the strongest hull in the Fleet.

The Future of the Type 21

There is much reason to believe that there is considerable life left in the hulls of the Type 21. They have seen a new lease of life with the hull strengthening, and the machinery is doing well. The easy replacement of the gas turbines has much to recommend it, but the rest of the machinery such as the gearboxes and shafts require careful monitoring and repair as necessary. Provided that this is done, the class could be seeing service in the 21st century — appropriate to their own type number! Increasingly over the next decade they are going to take on the burden of the day-to-day tasks of the Fleet as the 'Leander' class is paid off. To retain adequate numbers of frigates at sea it may become a requirement to extend the life of the class. If this becomes the case, then a number of enhancements must be considered in order to ensure that they remain credible as front-line warships.

Most importantly, the anti-aircraft capability must be updated. Seacat's performance against modern missiles and aircraft must be increasingly in doubt and it requires replacement. Twenty years ago at the design stage it was envisaged that the class would have the Seawolf missile, but that system proved bulkier and more costly than expected. Seawolf, a close-range self-defence missile, has however, proved most successful in Type 22s and modified 'Leanders', and might be the most effective option for the Type 21. This has become more feasible with the introduction of lightweight Seawolf.

Seawolf originally went to sea in the Type 22

Batch I and II frigates, together with the 'Leander' Batch IIIs as Guided Weapon System (GWS) 24 Mod O, using the radar tracker system Type 910. Later Type 22s are being fitted with an updated GWS 25 Mod 3, with a new tracking radar. A new system, GWS 26 Mod 1, has more recently been designed for the forthcoming Type 23 frigate and two auxiliary replenishment ships. This system is now at the end of its development programme, and is partially in production. A development of GWS 26, designated Mod 2, was initiated in 1988 with an order for development and production of a lightweight Seawolf, to be fitted in some Type 42 destroyers and the three 'Invincible' class aircraft carriers. It is likely to be at sea by the mid-1990s.

It would appear that this system might be ideal for the Type 21s, especially since the development costs will already have been borne by other classes.

Surveillance radars would require updating by replacement by either in-service radars or other commercially available radars.

Other, non-missile, close-range AA defence systems that might be considered include the Anglo-Dutch Goalkeeper, which is a fully-automated Gatling-type small calibre gun which fires 4,200 rounds per minute. This is currently entering service in the Type 42s and carriers. Alternatively, the US Phalanx system,

of a concept similar to that of Goalkeeper, might be fitted to Type 21s, possibly as they are removed from other RN ships.

At a lower-capability level there are suggestions that the provision of the smaller type of AA missile of the Javelin variety could be adapted for use at sea as a low-cost option. Further enhancement would come from the replacement of the Oerlikon 20mm mountings by the updated 20mm or 30mm guns which are currently in service in the newer ships of the Royal Navy.

With regard to ASW, the continued provision of a shipborne weapon system to attack sonar contacts should be seen as a high priority to keep the class fully viable in their anti-submarine role. Inevitably this requires the financial backing for fitting the updated STWS system. Yet again, there are no development costs involved in this provision, a vital factor in the constant striving to give value for money in defence procurement.

It can be seen that the Type 21 frigates can be kept as front-line warships carrying an impressive modern weapon fit with minimal research and development costs, should the requirement be there for their extended service.

It is of interest to turn our attention finally towards the next generation of frigates, both of MoD and UK commercial design, looking in

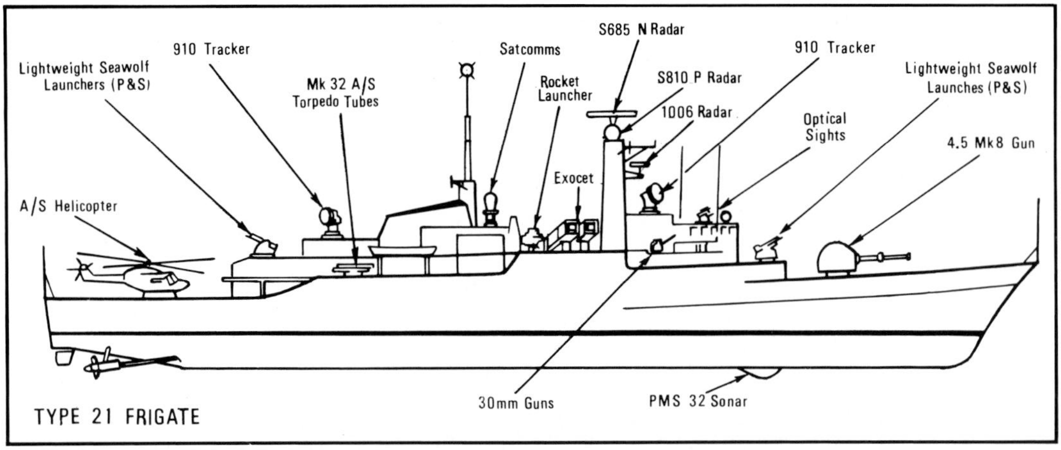
S685 N Radar
910 Tracker
Satcomms
910 Tracker
Lightweight Seawolf Launchers (P&S)
Mk 32 A/S Torpedo Tubes
Rocket Launcher
S810 P Radar
Lightweight Seawolf Launches (P&S)
1006 Radar
Optical Sights
4.5 Mk8 Gun
Exocet
A/S Helicopter
30mm Guns
PMS 32 Sonar
TYPE 21 FRIGATE

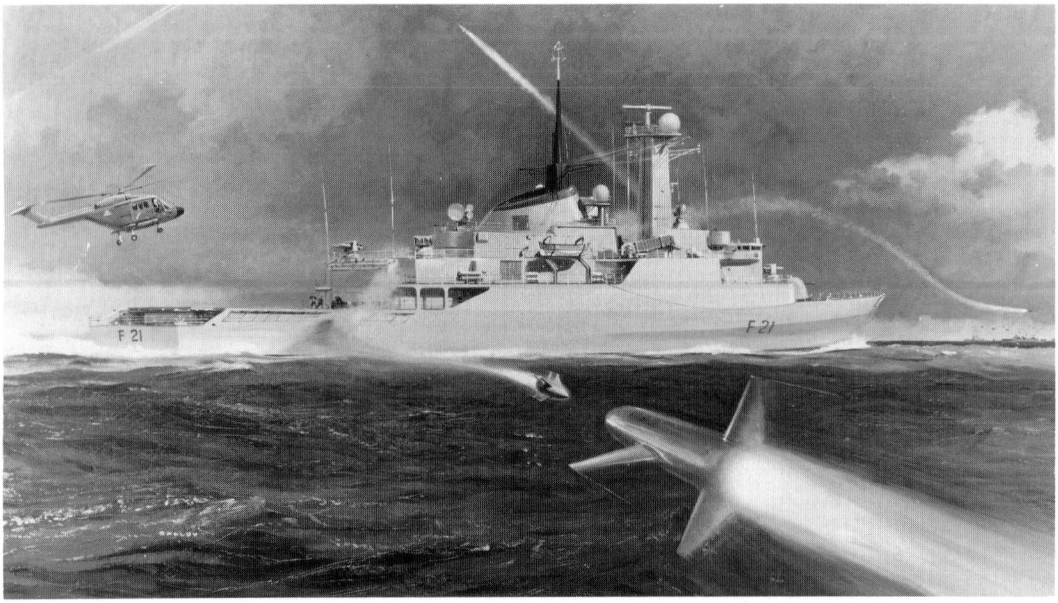

particular at how the lessons of the Type 21 have been incorporated.

Vosper Thornycroft Seawolf Type 21

In the very early days of the Type 21, VT continued their studies as to how to upgrade the weapon fit. In 1975 they announced their design for an improved Type 21 fitted with a 'double-headed' Seawolf system — in other words, one with two independent missile systems, one forward and one aft. The advantage of the design was that, although the new weapon fit represented a significant advance, the ship was of a fully proven design, and all the major components of the new systems had been already proven by extensive trials.

The new system comprised a forward and aft sub-system, each having two twin-barrelled lightweight launchers mounted port and starboard. These launchers had been developed using the land-based Rapier SAM system of launching rails instead of the container system used in the GWS 25 Seawolf system. Loading the launchers was to be carried out from below decks, and each launcher had its own magazine of 10 missiles; these could be topped up by replenishment at sea.

The Type 910 radar tracker of the GWS 25 was to be used, and two new surveillance radars to replace the Type 992 were proposed in order to utilise the full potential of the Seawolf system and to give optimum detection of high-speed sea-skimming missiles. All radars were to be fully interfaced with the CAAIS computer for action information, and

the Seawolf could be fired in an 'Auto' or 'Manual' mode.

Most regrettably, this excellent weapon fit could not be fitted into existing Type 21 hulls because of its additional size. For stability and reasons of space the design incorporated an increased beam of 2ft, not dissimilar to the increase of beam given to the Batch III 'Leander' class. Additionally, the ship's superstructure on 01 deck abreast both the Operations Room and the hangar would have been extended to the ship's side. The Exocet launchers would have been resited above, on 02 deck abaft the foremast, in a similar configuration to that on the Brazilian Mk 10 frigates.

Despite the potency of this new design, there were no orders for the Seawolf Type 21. The Royal Navy was pursuing the Type 22 and later the Type 23, and interest from overseas was never substantiated. The design proved the basis for further developments, which currently take the form of the 'Command Frigate' discussed later.

Type 23

The Type 23 was announced by the Government in 1980 as a cheap frigate to follow on from the Type 22. Initially expected to cost some £67 million and to be of around 3,000 tons, there have subsequently been a significant number of changes in design, not least to incorporate lessons learnt from the Falklands campaign. The design has been altered to incorporate a hangar and to operate the Sea King anti-submarine helicopter and its

successor the large EH101. A second Spey gas turbine has also been added. The class has seen an increase in tonnage to nearer 4,000 tons, and the cost of the first ship is said to be around £120 million. £67 million in 1980 is equivalent to £110 million at 1987/88 price levels, so it is apparent that a lot of extra value has been achieved for a very small amount of additional cost. Relative to its predecessor, the Type 22, the Type 23 is 'cheap', for four of the latter can be bought for the cost of three of the former. It will also be less expensive to operate, with a crew of about 180 compared with 260 on the Type 22.

HMS *Norfolk*, the first of the class, was laid down in 1985 and was accepted to come into service in late-1989. The class, designed primarily for the ASW role, is the backbone of the frigate replacement programme. Three further hulls were laid down in 1987, three of the class were ordered in 1988, with three more at the end of 1989.

Commercial Frigate Development

Not surprisingly, commercial frigate design has also kept pace with the advances in technology and tactics. Disappointed but not deterred by the lack of orders for the Seawolf Type 21 design, Vosper Thornycroft (VT) carried on with the concept of using the well-proven Type 21 as the basis for development.

VT's operational and marketing studies identified the worldwide need for two types of frigate. Firstly, what they called a Command Frigate, able to co-ordinate fleet and amphibious operations, and yet fully capable of operating alone against any threat; secondly, they saw a need for a smaller, cheaper General Purpose Frigate. This would be capable of deep-sea operations, and able to accept a wide variety of weapon fits that could be easily changed. Both these designs came directly from the Type 21.

The Command Frigate could easily be mistaken for the *Amazon* class in design, though not in capability. Using updated sensors and computers, it can have eight surface-to-surface missiles, the Phalanx *C*lose *In Weapon System* (CIWS) forward and aft, and the vertical-launched Seawolf. The Type 21's COGOG propulsion system is available, or alternatively CODOG — the use of diesel or gas. The increased beam allows the superstructure to be steel; extra accommodation includes provision for an Admiral and 13 staff officers.

The VT General Purpose Light Frigate, designated Type 18, is a more radical departure in ship design. Although 9m shorter, its hull form is a derivative of the Type 21 form. It is, however, relatively longer, with a 12% smaller volumetric coefficient to improve further the sea-keeping and hydrodynamic performance.

It is interesting to note that VT claims that the increase in relative length allows a reduction in the size of the superstructure, thus giving a long, low profile which in turn produces the advantage of a reduced radar-reflective area, reduced windage and a more effective weapons layout.

A low radar profile is extremely important, in that it makes the ship more difficult to detect,

and increases the effectiveness of the ship's electronic countermeasure systems. The shape of the hull and superstructure affect the radar-reflective pattern, and VT have introduced a below-deck hangar for the Lynx helicopter.

In order to give maximum flexibility to the customer, weapons and sensors for the Type 18 have not been specified; however, they include the Mk 8 4.5in gun, eight SSM, a SAM and CIWS system, the Lynx helicopter, and STWS. The upper deck layout allows the weapons to be sited in prime positions offering the widest arcs of fire. This is an impressive fit for a ship of this size. It is also designed to have a particularly small complement of 119 officers and men, an important feature for most navies. Propulsion is by three diesel engines which can give 30kt, but if a higher speed is required CODAG could be incorporated. The forward-looking nature of the Type 18 design, using the sea-keeping and ship performance of the Type 21, should give it an important position in the inventory of frigate design.

Left:
Norfolk at sea on sea-trials, with Red Ensign flying. This shot, taken in 1989, shows the 'Leander' class frigate *Penelope*, one of the oldest frigates of the RN, having a close look at the latest addition to the fleet. The different lines can be appreciated immediately. *MoD*

Below:
VT's Command Frigate shows the lines familiar to the Type 21. The hull is basically the same length and design, but the Seawolf silos are situated forward of the bridge. *Vosper Thornycroft*

Bottom:
Shorter in length and considerably lighter, the VT General Purpose Light Frigate shows sleek lines but a considerable armament. The hull design is again based on the Type 21. *Vosper Thornycroft*

HMS *Amazon*   F169

The first of the class, *Amazon* was launched by HRH The Princess Anne on 26 April 1971 at Woolston Yard, Southampton. Commissioned in May 1974, she underwent trials for the next year, both in UK waters and on the trials ranges in the West Indies. She went on to visit ports in Europe before commencing her first work-up at Portland in November 1975. The following year saw her exercising in the North Atlantic and Mediterranean, and she was one of the newest ships to be seen at the Silver Jubilee Review in 1977, just before she deployed to the Far East. It was in November of that year that she had a serious fire in her starboard Olympus module. Having steamed 121,234 miles, she entered refit in June 1978, and emerged in May the next year to undergo sea training and deployments to the Mediterranean and the West Indies. She carried out the Armilla patrol in the Gulf in 1982 before arriving off the Falklands in August. A year later she underwent a restorative refit (mileage 271,579), completing in September 1984. From July to December 1985 she deployed again to the South Atlantic, and then was one of four warships that went around the world on the 'Global '86' deployment. A full operational year in 1987 ended with a docking period, with just under 400,000 miles steamed.

Affiliations

Adopted by Southampton and North Tyneside.
The WRNS' ship.
14/20th Hussars.
206 Squadron RAF Kinloss.
39 Itchen North (Amazon) Sea Scouts.
TS *Amazon*, Hinckley, Leicestershire.
TS *Courageous*, Canterbury, Kent.
King's College, Taunton.
St Luke's Hospice, Plymouth.

Origins of name: One of a mythical tribe of warlike women who fought against the Greek Heroes. They cut off their right breasts to fire their bows, and they killed their baby boys, raising only girls.

Crest: An Amazon's head in gold on a red field.

Motto: Audaciter — Boldly.

Previous Amazons

1 Prize (*Panthère*) taken in 1745. Sold in 1763.
2 Prize (*Subtile*) taken in 1746.
3 Frigate of 1773. Broken up in 1794.
4 Frigate of 1795. Wrecked after action in 1797.
5 Frigate of 1799. Flew Nelson's flag. Sold in 1812.
6 5th Rate of 1821. Sold in 1863.
7 Sloop of 1865. Sunk in collision in 1866.
8 Destroyer of 1908. Sold in 1919.
9 Destroyer of 1926. Broken up in 1948.

Battle Honours

Martinique	1762
Droits de L'Homme	1797
Copenhagen	1801
Belle Poule	1806
Belgian Coast	1914-16
Atlantic	1939-43
Norway	1940
Arctic	1942
Malta Convoys	1942
North Africa	1942-43

HMS *Antelope* F170

HMS *Antelope* was the second of the class, being launched in 1972 at Vosper's Woolston Yard by Lady Kirk, the wife of the Under Secretary of State for the Royal Navy. She commissioned at Southampton in 1975 into the Sixth Frigate Squadron, and underwent trials and work-up. Two years later she joined the 11-ship Group Five deployment to the Western Atlantic, visiting Argentina amongst many other countries. That year she also visited St Nazaire to mark the 34th anniversary of the raid by HMS *Campbeltown*. She took part in the Silver Jubilee Fleet Review at Spithead in 1977. Subsequently, as Belize guardship, she acted as plane guard escort to HMS *Ark Royal* during the carrier's last deployment to the Caribbean, and later visited Bermuda with HMS *Blake*. In 1979 she visited a number of North European ports during exercises with Federal German Navy ships. Later, with HMS *Jupiter*, she made a rare visit to Constanta in Romania, before beginning a 10-month refit.

She visited France after her re-dedication in March 1980, and then began another spell as Belize guardship. It was during that West Indies deployment that she hit the headlines by seizing £30 million worth of marijuana on-board a Panamanian coaster in Belize waters.

One of the earliest ships to arrive in the South Atlantic in 1982, she was hit by two 1,000lb bombs whilst supporting the amphibious operations in San Carlos Water. Although neither detonated, the attempt to defuse one of the bombs was unsuccessful: the explosion and subsequent fire caused her eventually to sink.

Roll of Honour

M. R. Stephens (18) STD. Missing, presumed dead.
J. Prescott (37) S/Sgt. Killed while attempting to defuse a bomb in the ship.

Affiliations

City of Hereford (Freedom of city granted in 1980).
Royal Regiment of Fusiliers.
Sea Cadet Corps: Hereford and Middlesbrough.

Crest: The head of an antelope.

Motto: Audax et vigilans — Daring and watchful.

Previous Antelopes (Anthelope)
1 Galleon of 1546. Burnt in 1649.
2 Galleon of 1651. Wrecked in 1652.
3 Galleon of 1654.
4 Galleon of 1660 (ex *Preson*). Sold in 1693.
5 4th Rate of 1703. Broken up in 1783.
6 4th Rate of 1802-1848. Became a convict ship.
7 Iron paddlesteamer sloop of 1848. Sold in 1883.
8 Torpedo Gunboat of 1843-1919.
9 Destroyer of 1929. Broken up in 1946.

Battle Honours

Armada	1588
Lowestoft	1665
Four Days' Battle	1666
Orfordness	1666
Solebay	1672
Banky Bay	1680
Guadeloupe	1690
Marbella	1705
Ostend	1804
Atlantic	1939-44
Bismarck Action	1941
Malta Convoys	1942
North Africa	1942-43
Falkland Islands	1982

HMS *Active*   F171

The present HMS *Active* was launched in 1972 at Vosper Thornycroft's Southampton Yard, but was not commissioned until 1977. This delay was due to financial wrangling between Vosper Thornycroft and the Ministry of Defence. *Active's* first 12 months were spent working-up and carrying out weapon trials, before deploying to the east coast of the USA and Canada in July 1978. In January 1979 she sailed to escort the Royal Yacht on a five-month tour of the Middle East, and subsequently joined NATO's on-call naval force in the Mediterranean.

During 1980 the ship was mainly home-based, but deployed to the West Indies, as guardship, for three months at the end of the year. After a period of operating in UK waters, November 1981 saw *Active* in the Middle East again, this time for the Armilla patrol in the Gulf. Whilst on the way home in the spring of 1982 *Active*, like many other ships, found herself retasked to take part in the Falklands campaign.

After a second tour of duty in the Falklands in 1983, *Active* returned home for routine docking and to prepare for a five-month deployment to the West Indies in March 1984. During this tour the ship was involved in exercises with the US Navy, and fired six Exocet missiles on the American missile test ranges. In May 1985 *Active* commenced a mid-life refit, sailing in August 1986 for post-refit trials and work-up. In mid-1987 she sailed once again for the Armilla patrol, and during this tour of increased tension the ship accompanied 35 ships, totalling over 3.5 million tons, through the Straits of Hormuz. In the latter part of 1987 *Active* took part in exercise Purple Warrior, the largest amphibious exercise undertaken by the UK for many years.

Affiliations

Burnley.
Queen's Lancashire Regiment.
TS *Lookout* (Burnley).
TS *Active* (Southport).
TS (JCC) *Active* (Waterlooville).
Lancing College.
Mount Tamar College.
48 Burnley Worsthorne St John's Brownies.

Crest: A gold saliant chamois on a field of blue.

Motto: Festina Lente — Hasten slowly.

Previous Actives

1 Frigate of 1758. Captured in 1778.
2 Brig — sloop of 1776. Captured in 1780.

3 Cutter of 1779. Captured in 1779.
4 Frigate of 1780. Wrecked in 1796.
5 Brig — sloop. In service 1782.
6 5th Rate of 1799. Renamed *Argo* in 1833.
7 5th Rate of 1846. Renamed *Durham* in 1867.
8 Corvette of 1869. Sold in 1906. Said to have been the last large man-of-war to proceed out of Portsmouth under sail.
9 Cruiser of 1911. Sold in 1920.
10 Destroyer of 1929. Broken up in 1948.

Battle Honours

Lagos	1759
Trincomalee	1782
Camperdown	1797
Egypt	1801
Lissa	1811
Pelagosa	1811
Ashantee	1873-74
Jutland	1916
Atlantic	1939-44
Bismark	1941
Diego Suarez	1942
Arctic	1944
Falkland Islands	1982

HMS *Ambuscade*   F172

This was the fourth of the class, launched in January 1973 at Yarrow's Scotstoun Shipyard by Lady Griffin, wife of the Controller of the Navy. Accepted into service in August 1975,

Right:
They say 'worse things happen at sea', and they do! Shortly after a collision with a USN cruiser in the Arabian Sea during high speed manoeuvres, *Ambuscade* lies stopped in the water with a 20ft gash in her bows. Under her own steam the ship got to Bombay, where a new bow was built. *Lt R. Finnemore*

she was formally commissioned at Devonport on 5 September 1975. The normal sea trials and work-up took her to mid-1976, and then patrols, exercises and maintenance filled the programme until she joined the STANAVFOR-LANT in March 1977. That deployment involved countless exercises and visits on both sides of the Atlantic. A docking period completed 1977 before work-up and a major five-month deployment to the Western Atlantic and Pacific via the Panama Canal with HMS *Blake* and the 5th Frigate Squadron, of which she was a member. 1979 saw operations around the UK and a spell as West Indies guardship (WIGS) in the Caribbean. Home for Christmas, she commenced a 10-month refit in April 1980, having steamed over 150,000 miles. A standard programme in 1981 led up to deployment in October to the Gulf for the Armilla patrol. Returning home in late February 1982, she turned around in five weeks and headed south for the Falklands War, finally returning to the UK in late July. Early in 1983 she sailed for another Armilla patrol, during which she had a collision with the US cruiser *Dale* which necessitated a new bow being built in Bombay. She then continued her deployment to the Far East. Home in August, she was off to WIGS in November until February 1984, entering refit in October (289,500 miles steamed). This lasted through into 1986, and in October she headed to the South Atlantic for a five-month spell as guardship, getting back in March 1987. She has remained operational since then.

Affiliations

Crewe and Nantwich.
The Cheshire Regiment (22nd of Foot).
TS *Ambuscade* (Crewe).
TS *Aberconwy* (Llandudno).
TS *Indomitable* (Nottingham).
Ampleforth School.
151 Squadron, RAF Chivenor.
Homeleigh House, Crewe.

Origins of name: 'Ambuscade' is an old English name for an ambush. Taken from the French ship *Embuscade*, captured by HMS *Defiance* in 1746.

Crest: A brown blunderbuss with barrel and mounts in gold and silver, on a black field.

Motto: Tempori insidior — I bide my time.

Previous Ambuscades:
1 5th Rate. Prize (*Embuscade*) taken in 1746. Sold in 1762.
2 5th Rate of 1773. Captured by French in 1748, recaptured as *Embuscade* by HMS *Victory* in 1803. Broken up in 1810.
3 5th Rate. Prize (*Embuscade*) taken in 1798 and added to Fleet in 1799 as *Ambuscade*, but renamed HMS *Seine* when previous *Embuscade* was recaptured.

4 5th Rate (*Pomone*) captured in 1811. Broken up in 1812.
5 5th Rate. Renamed *Amphion* prior to launch and converted to steam.
6 Destroyer of 1913. Sold in 1921.
7 Destroyer of 1926. Broken up in 1947.

Battle Honours:

Finnisterre	1747
Lagos	1759
Jutland	1916
Atlantic	1940-44
Arctic	1942
Falkland Islands	1982

HMS *Arrow* F173

Another Yarrow's ship, HMS *Arrow* was launched on Clydeside on 5 February 1974 by Lady Raper, wife of Vice-Adm Sir George Raper, the Director General of Ships. *Arrow* was the fifth Type 21, and the first to carry Exocet missiles. She was handed over at Devonport in May 1976 before commissioning into the Third Frigate Squadron on 29 July 1976 in Sunderland, the town to which she is affiliated. Trials followed in home and European waters through into 1977, when she visited the Mediterranean for a sales tour and attended the Jubilee Review at Spithead. In 1978 she acted as guardship to the Royal Yacht, and from May to December the following year she deployed to the Far East and Australia with a group of RN ships. A restorative refit came next and included hull strengthening and the fitting of STWS torpedo tubes. In 1981 she joined STANAVFORLANT, taking part in the major exercise 'Ocean Venture '81' between August and October. In spring 1982 she was exercising off Gibraltar with other RN units when the Falkland Islands were invaded, and she was in the first wave of ships to go south. She went alongside the stricken HMS *Sheffield* and spent several hours fighting to save her and to rescue survivors. Returning from the South Atlantic she entered refit, emerging in September 1983 for trials and work-up before setting sail for the Falklands again in April 1984. She acted as West Indies guardship in 1987, returning for Christmas and to start a further refit in 1988. She has steamed 397,459 miles.

Affiliations
Sunderland.
15/19 King's Hussars.
4th Field Regiment Royal Artillery.
Red Arrows, RAF.
TS *Blackcap* (Birkenhead).

TS *Arrow* (Chesham).
1st Connidown Cub Scout Pack.
Harrow School.
Royal Company of Archers.
Various Sunderland charities.

Crest: Two crossed gold arrows, feathered red, on a field of green.

Motto: Celeriter certus — Swiftly sure.

Previous Arrows:
1 Sloop of 1796. Captured in 1805.
2 Cutter of 1805. Broken up in 1828.
3 Cutter of 1823. Broken up in 1852.
4 Gun vessel of 1854. Sold in 1862.
5 Steam gunboat of 1871. Sold in 1922.
6 Destroyer of 1929. Damaged beyond repair in 1943. Broken up 1949.

Battle Honours:

Copenhagen	1801
Cape Tenez	1805
San Sebastian	1813
Black Sea	1854-55
Atlantic	1940-43
Norway	1940
North Sea	1942
Libya	1942
Malta Convoys	1942
Sicily	1943
Falkland Islands	1982

HMS *Alacrity* F174

Laid down at Yarrow's in 1973, *Alacrity* was launched into the Clyde by Lady McKaig, wife of Adm Sir Rae McKaig, in September 1974. Following acceptance in April 1977, she began her first commission in the Third Frigate Squadron in July 1977. Participating in the Spithead Fleet Review that year, she then embarked on her trials and work-up to become fully operational. In 1979 she transferred to the First Frigate Squadron and then deployed the following year for a Group Deployment around the world. Included in this was a visit to the Yangtse river — the first for 30 years. A spell in the Gulf on patrol preceded her return to the UK in December 1980. An operational programme the next year included the major NATO exercise 'Ocean Safari' in the North Atlantic. 1982 saw *Alacrity* fully involved in the Falklands War, during which she received minor damage whilst going alongside the sinking *Atlantic Conveyor* to rescue the crew.

The first frigate back from the war, she deployed again in September 1982 for the Armilla patrol in the Gulf. 1984 was partially taken up with an extended docking period to refurbish her and fit the ship's side strengthening. She deployed in February 1984 to the South Atlantic and Falkland Islands guardship and then to the West Indies the following year, again as the guardship. She paid off in March

1986 for her first refit in nine years, having steamed 313,000 miles. This restorative refit included a trial in which the ship's company was reduced from 100 to about 20 men. Whilst there was an obvious saving in manpower, the scheme was not hailed as particularly successful, being harder than usual to bring the ship out of dockyard hands to become operational again. Trials were completed at the end of 1987, and she is now fully running with a busy programme.

Affiliations
Winchester.
The Royal Green Jackets.
CCF, RGS Worcester.
TS *Alacrity* (Glasgow).
TS *Itchen* (Winchester).
Greenacres Special School, Winchester.
The Mermaid Theatre, London.

Crest: A red heart with golden wings on a field of silver.

Motto: Adjuvare propero — I hasten to help.

Previous Alacritys:
1 Sloop of 1806. Captured by French in 1811.
2 Sloop of 1818. Sold for £660 in 1835.
3 Despatch vessel of 1856. Broken up in 1864.
4 Survey schooner of 1872. Sold in 1882.
5 Despatch vessel of 1885. Sold in 1913.
6 Despatch vessel of 1885 under name of *Surprise*. Renamed *Alacrity* in 1913. Sold in 1919.
7 Yacht of differing names including *Mlada*, owned by a Russian princess. 1919-22 renamed *Alacrity* for naval service on China station, then handed back to original owners.
8 Sloop of 1944. Broken up 1956.

Battle Honours:

China	1900
Korea	1950-52
Falkland Islands	1982

HMS *Ardent* F184

HMS *Ardent*, the seventh of the class, was launched by the Duchess of Gloucester in May 1975. Built by Yarrow's at Glasgow, she arrived at Devonport in September 1977 and was handed over the same day, commissioning into the Sixth Frigate Squadron in October that year. She was the first Type 21 to be fitted with a ship-launched torpedo weapon system (STWS). Her trials and work-up period were

Affiliations

Milford Haven.
Second Battalion Scots Guards.
TS *Ardent* (Macclesfield).

HMS *Ardent* Association

Following the loss of the ship, members of the ship's company formed the *Ardent* Association 'to continue the spirit that had developed in the ship since she first commissioned'. Additionally, the Association aims to perpetuate the memory of fallen shipmates, and to keep in close contact with their families, all of whom are members. Along with these families, membership is open to all officers and ratings who served in *Ardent* at any time, and to those people who have the Association's best interests at heart.

Each year, in May, a memorial service and reunion are held in Plymouth. The service takes place in St Nicholas' Church, HMS *Drake*, where the ship's bell is held, together with a plaque commemorating the loss of *Ardent* and *Antelope*. The bell was found by divers quite some distance from the ship, having suffered severe fire damage. It is a tradition in the Royal Navy for members of the ships' companies to have their children baptised in their ship's bells, and many of *Ardent's* survivors' children born since 1982 have been baptised in her bell.

Crest: A torch on a field of grey.

Motto: Through fire and water.

Previous Ardents:
1   3rd Rate of 1764. Sold in 1784.
2   3rd Rate of 1782. Blown up in 1794.
3   3rd Rate of 1796. Broken up in 1824.
4   Sloop of 1841. Broken up in 1864.
5   Destroyer of 1894. Sold in 1911.

followed by a deployment in the autumn of 1978 to the Baltic with the Sixth Frigate Squadron. She sailed to the Red Sea in January 1979, and later in the year took part in the major NATO exercise 'Highwood' in the Atlantic. Early in 1980 she joined STANAVFORLANT, taking part among 40 ships in another NATO exercise 'Safe Pass'. She went on with the force to visit the east coast of the USA. She took part in the newly established Armilla Gulf patrol over Christmas 1980, during which she steamed her 100,000th mile. Returning in mid-1981, she visited her affiliated town, attended Plymouth Navy Days, and acted as guardship for Cowes Week. One of her last foreign visits came before Christmas 1981, when she visited Amsterdam with three other Type 21 frigates. An exercise in 1982 took her to Norwegian waters, and there she laid a wreath off the coast over the spot where her namesake lies. She sailed south in April 1982 with the Falklands Task Force, and was sunk on 21 May 1982 in the Falklands Sound when struck by bombs during heavy attacks by Pucara, Skyhawk and Mirage aircraft.

Roll of Honour

6 Destroyer of 1913. Sunk at Jutland in 1916.
7 Destroyer of 1929. Sunk in action in 1940.
                    (Motto seems rather appropriate.)

Battle Honours:

Toulon	1793
Camperdown	1797
Copenhagen	1801
Buenos Aires	1807
Black Sea	1854-55
Jutland	1916
Atlantic	1939-40
Norway	1940
Falkland Islands	1982

HMS *Avenger* F185

The youngest of the class, *Avenger* was laid down in October 1974 at Yarrow's and launched the following year in November by Mrs Judd, the wife of the Navy Minister. Completed in April 1978, she commissioned at Devonport the next month and then underwent extensive trials and work-up. Sailing in mid-January 1980 for the West Indies and the North Atlantic, she was diverted to the Mediterranean for three months because of the situation in Afghanistan. Towards the end of 1980 she deployed to the Gulf for the Armilla patrol, which lasted the standard five months. A year later she headed for the West Indies, where she spent two and a half months as guardship (WIGS). The start of the Falklands War found her sitting in the bottom of a dock in Devonport, but she got ready in very short time and sailed on 10 May. She was one of the last ships to return from the war, getting back in September 1982. In March 1983 she was off again, back to the Armilla patrol. During this patrol, her helicopter crashed into the sea off Oman. The crew, together with the ship's Captain, who was a passenger, were injured but were rescued. The deployment continued and the ship, together with *Ambuscade*, visited the Far East before returning in August. There followed WIGS from January to March 1984, and then a docking period in Devonport. 1985 started in the Mediterranean, followed by five months as guardship in the South Atlantic. A final spell as WIGS started 1986 before she started her restorative refit in September 1986, having steamed 297,656 miles. This lasted through into 1988, and she started sea trials in March that year.

Affiliations

Borough of Restormel, Cornwall.
13th/18th Royal Hussars (Queen Mary's Own).
TS *Hood* (St Austell).

TS *Exmouth* (Exmouth).
JCC *Avenger* (Cowplain).
Bradmean School, Exeter.

Crest: A pair of hands, gauntleted proper, grasping a double-handed sword in bend sinister gold, enflamed proper, on a field of argent.

Motto: None.

Previous Avengers:
1 Sloop of 1779. Sold in 1783.
2 Sloop. Prize taken in 1794. Sold in 1802, foundered in 1803.
3 Sloop purchased in 1803. Foundered same year.
4 Sloop purchased in 1804. Wrecked in 1812.
5 Frigate of 1845. Wrecked in 1847.
6 Armed merchant cruiser of 1915. Torpedoed in 1917.
7 Escort carrier of 1940, transferred to RN under Lend-Lease in 1942. Torpedoed in 1942.
8 Landing ship named in 1947. Sold to India in 1949 and still in service.
                    (Author's note: 'I'm glad I commanded *Amazon*!')

Battle Honours:

Martinique	1794
Arctic	1942
North Africa	1942
Falkland Islands	1982

Appendix 2
Ship Details

Displacement (tonnes): 2,750 standard; 3,250 full load
Length, ft (m): 360 (104.7) waterline; 384 (117) overall
Beam, ft (m): 41.8 (12.7)
Draught, ft (m): 19 (5.8)
Propulsion:
COGOG
  2×RR Olympus TM 3B gas turbines, each 25,000shp
  2×RR Tyne RMIC gas turbines, each 5,000shp

Speed: 30kt on Olympus
      18kt on Tyne

Range: 4,000 miles at 17kt
      1,200 miles at 30kt

Below:
Avenger **ploughs into the swell. Seakeeping characteristics of the Type 21 are similar to, if not slightly better than, those of the 'Leander' class.**
MoD

Appendix 3
Weapon Details

Missiles
Anti-Ship Missiles (ASM)
Exocet (GWS 50)
Range: Min 4.5km, Max 42-45km
Dimensions: Length 5.21m, Span 1.0m,
Diameter 34.8cm
Speed: M0.93
Propulsion: Boost: 2.4sec burn
              Sustain: 93sec burn
Control: Cruciform rear fins
Guidance: Cruise and radio altimeter
Attack: Single axis radar seeker
Payload: 165kg blast/fragmentation warhead
          Delay and proximity fuse

Sea Skua (Lynx helicopter carries maximum
of four)
Range: 14km
Dimensions: Length 2.5m, Span 72cm,
Diameter 25cm
Speed: High subsonic
Propulsion: Solid fuel separate boost and
sustainer motors

Control: Cruciform canard fins
Guidance: Semi-active radar and radio
altimeter
Payload: 35kg HE

Surface to Air Missiles (SAM)
Seacat (GWS 24)
Range: 5km
Dimensions: Length 1.47m, Span 65cm,
Diameter 19cm
Speed: M0.9
Propulsion: Dual-thrust solid fuel
Control: Cruciform rear fins
Guidance: TV auto and manual guidance
Payload: Blast HE warhead with proximity fuze
Associated radar: Type 912 Tracker, with TV

Below:
**Ardent in company with a supertanker in the
Straits of Hormuz at the entrance of the Gulf in
1981. The RN has maintained a patrol in this area
for over nine years.** *MoD*

Guns

4.5in Mk 8
Calibre: 113mm
Range: 23km
Muzzle velocity: 868.7m/sec
Rate of fire: 25 rounds/min
Shells: Weight 21kg; HE warhead 2.53kg
      Starshell 600,000 candelas for 40sec
      Chaff
      Practice: Surface and AA
Associated radar: Type 912 tracker

Oerlikon 20mm
4 single mountings
Range: 1,100m
Rate of fire: 450 rounds/min

Anti-Submarine Weapons
Ship Torpedo Weapon System (STWS)
2 triple torpedo tubes, carrying Mk 44 or 46
torpedo

Sensors

Radars
Type 992: E/F Band. Surveillance
Type 1006: I Band. Navigation and helicopter
control
Type 912: I Band. Gunnery and Seacat trackers
Type 1010/1011: Interrogation Friend or Foe
(IFF). Secondary radar

Sonars
Type 184: Medium-range active sonar, with
limited passive capability
Type 162: Short-range bottom-search sonar
Type 2015: Bathythermograph
Type 182: Torpedo decoy
Type 185 or Type 2008/2009: Underwater
communications

Below:
**The refurbished HMS *Warrior* under tow to
Portsmouth. *Arrow* salutes the past, making a
distinct contrast to the last century's
revolutionary warship.** *MoD*

Electronic warfare
Outfit UAA 1: Electronic countermeasures
equipment
Outfit FH5: Direction finder

Computers
CAAIS: DBS (2), Ferranti FM 1600 B
Weapon Control: DBD (1), Ferranti FM 1600 B
      WSA 4 consists of GSA 4
      with the 4.5in gun and GWS
      24 with Seacat
WAS: Weapon Assessment System
OASIS: Stores, catering and word processing
HP 9825: Desktop computer for Link 14 and
many programs

Data Links
Link 10: HF and VHF transmit and receive
Link 14: receive facility only

Communications
Integrated Communications System 2 (ICS 2)
Satellite Communications Terminal UK/SSC
002 (SCOT)
    (fitted according to operational requirement)
V/UHF equipment

Helicopter
Lynx HAS Mk 2
Length oa: 15.2m
Length — blades and tail folded: 10.6m
Width — blades folded: 3.7m
Height — rotors running: 3.6m
Main rotor diameter: 12.8m
Tail rotor diameter: 2.2m
Maximum take-off wt: 4,535kg
Cruising speed: 125kt
Max speed: 160kt
Powered by 2 RR Gem engines

Weapons
2 Mk 44, 46 or Stingray torpedoes
2 depth charges
4 Sea Skua ASM